CW00348081

MICHELIN
GUIDE

NORDIC COUNTRIES

DENMARK I FINLAND I ICELAND
NORWAY I SWEDEN

MICHELIN

DEAR READER,

We are delighted to introduce the fifth edition of the Michelin guide to the Nordic Countries – a guide to the best places to eat and stay in Denmark, Finland, Iceland, Norway and Sweden. Alongside restaurants and hotels in the main cities, we are also pleased to recommend a selection of our favourite places from smaller towns and villages.

The guide caters for every type of visitor, from business traveller to holiday maker, and highlights the best establishments, from cosy bistros and intimate townhouses to celebrated restaurants and luxury hotels.

The Michelin inspectors are the eyes and ears of our readers and their anonymity is key to ensuring that they receive the same treatment as any other guest. Each year, they search for new establishments to add to the guide, and only the best make it through. Once the annual selection has been made, the 'best of the best' are then recognised with Michelin Stars ❄ and Bib Gourmands ⊛.

Restaurants – our readers' favourite part – appear at the front of each locality, with the hotels following afterwards. Restaurants are ordered according to the quality of their food, with the Stars and Bib Gourmands placed at the top, followed by the Plates ⑩. Being chosen by the Michelin Inspectors for inclusion in the guide is a guarantee of quality in itself and the plate symbol highlights restaurants where you will get a good meal.

Our mission is to help you find the best restaurants and hotels on your travels. Please don't hesitate to contact us, as we are keen to hear your opinions on the establishments listed within these pages, as well as those you feel could be of interest for future editions.

We trust you will enjoy travelling with the 2018 edition of our Nordic Countries guide.

CONTENTS

THE MICHELIN GUIDE'S COMMITMENTS

EXPERIENCED IN QUALITY

Whether they are in Japan, the USA, China or Europe, our inspectors use the same criteria to judge the quality of each and every restaurant and hotel that they visit. The Michelin guide commands a worldwide reputation thanks to the commitment we make to our readers - and we reiterate these below:

➡ ANONYMOUS INSPECTIONS

Our inspectors make regular and anonymous visits to restaurants and hotels to gauge the quality of products and services offered to an ordinary customer. They settle their own bill and may then introduce themselves and ask for more information about the establishment. Our readers' comments are also a valuable source of information, which we can follow up with a visit of our own.

➡ INDEPENDENCE

To remain totally objective for our readers, the selection is made with complete independence. Entry into the guide is free. All decisions are discussed with the Editor and our highest awards are considered at a European level.

foto@carstenmuller.com/G20

→ SELECTION AND CHOICE

The guide offers a selection of the best restaurants and hotels in every category of comfort and price. This is only possible because all the inspectors rigorously apply the same methods.

→ ANNUAL UPDATES

All the practical information, classifications and awards are revised and updated every year to give the most reliable information possible.

→ CONSISTENCY

The criteria for the classifications are the same in every country covered by the MICHELIN guide.

→ THE SOLE INTENTION OF MICHELIN IS TO MAKE YOUR TRAVELS SAFE AND ENJOYABLE.

QUALITY OF COOKING - THE DISTINCTIONS

❀❀❀ THREE STARS
Exceptional cuisine, worth a special journey!
Our highest award is given for the superlative cooking of chefs at the peak of their profession. The ingredients are exemplary, the cooking is elevated to an art form and their dishes are often destined to become classics.

❀❀ TWO STARS
Excellent cooking, worth a detour!
The personality and talent of the chef and their team is evident in the expertly crafted dishes, which are refined, inspired and sometimes original.

❀ ONE STAR
High quality cooking, worth a stop!
Using top quality ingredients, dishes with distinct flavours are carefully prepared to a consistently high standard.

☺ BIB GOURMAND
Good quality, good value cooking
'Bibs' are awarded for simple yet skilful cooking.

⭐○ PLATE
Good cooking
Fresh ingredients, capably prepared: simply a good meal.

SEEK AND SELECT...

RESTAURANTS

Restaurants are listed by distinction. Within each distinction category, they are then ordered alphabetically.

✿✿✿ **Three Stars:** Exceptional cuisine, worth a special journey!

✿✿ **Two Stars:** Excellent cooking, worth a detour!

✿ **One Star:** High quality cooking, worth a stop!

⊕ **Bib Gourmand:** Good quality, good value cooking

⍐O **Michelin Plate:** Good cooking

WHERE YOU ARE

Bottom of the page: country and town.

On the side: neighbourhood.

KADEAU COPENHAGEN ✿✿

▶ MODERN CUISINE • DESIGN • FASHIONABLE   ⅩⅹⅩ ◀

Wildersgade 10B ✉ 1408 K – PLAN: D3
Ⓜ Christianshavn
TEL. 33 25 22 23 – **www**.kadeau.dk
Closed 5 weeks July-August, 1 week Christmas and Sunday-Tuesday
Menu 1850 DKK (dinner only and Saturday lunch)
(tasting menu only) (booking essential)

Chef:
Nicolai Nørregaard
Specialities:
Garden vegetable terrine with tomato broth and cherry oil. Peas with mint and roasted nasturtium. Smoked celeriac, white asparagus and woodruff.

You'll receive a warm welcome at this delightful restaurant, where the open kitchen adds a sense of occasion to the sophisticated room. The chefs have an innate understanding of how best to match fresh and aged produce, and use their experience in preserving and fermenting to add many elements to each dish.

KEY WORDS

If you are looking for a specific type of establishment, these key words will help you make your choice more quickly.

• For restaurants, the first word relates to the type of cuisine and the second, to the atmosphere.

• For hotels, the first word explains the establishment type (chain, business, luxury, etc.); the second describes the décor (modern, stylish, design, etc.) and sometimes a third will be used to complete the picture.

COMFORT

Level of comfort from ⅩⅹⅩⅹⅩ to Ⅹ. Red: our most delightful places.

LOCATING THE ESTABLISHMENT

Location and coordinates on the town plan, with main sights

HOTELS

Hotels are listed by comfort, from 🏨🏨🏨 to 🏠. Within each comfort category, they are then ordered alphabetically.
Red: our most delightful places

FREDERIKSMINDE

🏠

COUNTRY HOUSE • ELEGANT • CLASSIC

PRÆSTØ

≪ ☺ ♨ ⋔ 🏛 🅿

Klosternakken 8 ✉ 4720
TEL. 55 90 90 30 – www.frederiksminde.com
Closed 23-26 December and 1-16 January
19 rm ⌂ – ♦ 1145 DKK ♦♦ 1545 DKK
FREDERIKSMINDE ☺ – See restaurant listing

An attractive 19C house named after a former king of Denmark; it has a classic, understated style and offers superb views. Bedrooms are tastefully furnished, well-kept and comfortable; antiques and fine portraits feature.

FACILITIES & SERVICES

⋔	Hotel with a restaurant
♿	Wheelchair access
AIC	Air conditioning (in all or part of the establishment)
🏠	Outside dining available
🆂🅿🅰 🛁	Spa • Sauna • Exercise room
🏊 🏊	Swimming pool: outdoor or indoor
🌿 🎾	Garden or park • Tennis court
🏛 ♢	Conference room • Private dining room
🕙	Restaurant offering lower priced theatre menus
🚗 🚘 🅿	Valet parking • Garage • Car park
💳̸	Credit cards not accepted
Ⓜ	Nearest metro station

OTHER SPECIAL FEATURES

☺	Peaceful establishment
≪	Great view
🍷	Particularly interesting wine list

9

Aflo/hemis.fr

DENMARK

DISTINCTIONS

COPENHAGEN

Denmark

J.-B. Rabouan/hemis.fr

Some cities overwhelm you, and give the impression that there's too much of them to take in. Not Copenhagen. Most of its key sights are neatly compressed within its central Slotsholmen 'island', an area that enjoyed its first golden age in the early seventeenth century in the reign of Christian IV, when it became a harbour of great consequence. It has canals on three sides and opposite the harbour is the area of Christianshavn, home of the legendary freewheeling 'free-town' community of Christiania. Further up from the centre are Nyhavn, the much-photographed canalside with brightly coloured

buildings where the sightseeing cruises leave from, and the elegant Frederiksstaden, whose wide streets contain palaces and museums. West of the centre is where Copenhageners love to hang out: the Tivoli Gardens, a kind of magical fairyland. Slightly more down-to-earth are the western suburbs of Vesterbro and Nørrebro, which were run-down areas given a street credible spit and polish for the 21C, and are now two of the trendiest districts. Once you've idled away some time in the Danish capital, you'll wonder why anyone might ever want to leave. With its waterfronts, quirky shops and cafés, the city presents a modern, user-friendly ambience – but it also boasts world class art collections, museums, and impressive parks, gardens and lakes, all of which bear the mark of an earlier time.

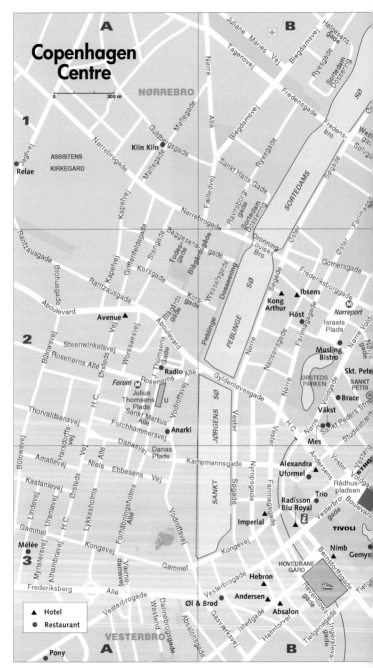

Copenhagen Centre

0 — 300 m

NØRREBRO

ASSISTENS
KIRKEGARD

Relae

Jagtvej

Juliane Maries Vej

Tagensvej

Helgesens-
gade

Blegdamsvej

Ryesgade

Sortedam
Dossering

Nørre Allé

Guldbergsgade

Møllegade

Nørrebrogade

Kiin Kiin

Kapelvej

Blegdamsvej

Sankt Hans Gade

Fredensgade

Fredens-
bro

SØ

Welt
gac
Solvga

Nørrebrogade

Fælledvej

Ravnsborg-
gade

Sortedam
Dossering

Dronning
Louises
Bro

SORTEDAMS

Øster

Østen

Farimags

Rantzausgade

Brohusgade

Griffenfeldsgade

Stengade

Todes-
gade

Blågårdsgade

Wesselsgade

Korsgade

Dosseering

Gothersgade

Frederiksborggade

Aboulevard

Rantzausvej

Kapelvej

Korsgade

Blågårds-
gade

SØ

Segade

Nørreport

Israels
Plads

Norre Void

Nor

Avenue

Ibsens

Kong
Arthur

Høst

Bülowsvej

Rosenørns Allé

Steenwinkelsvej

Worsaaesvej

Østeds Vej

Thomsens
Gade

Aboulevard

Rosenørns Allé

PEBLINGE

SØ

Nansensgade

Nørre

Musling
Bistro

Skt. Petr

SANKT
PETRI

Brace

ØRSTEDS
PARKEN

H.C.

Thorvaldsensvej

Harsdorffs Vej

Østeds Vej

Radio

Forum

Julius
Thomsens
Plads

Sankt Markus
Alle

Forchhammersvej

Danasvej

Anarki

JØRGENS

SØ

Vester

H.C.

Nørre

Vester

Norre

Sankt Peders Stra

Studiestra

V35

Vækst

Mes

Amalievej

Niels Ebbesens Vej

Danas
Plads

Kampmannsgade

Nyropsgade

Farimagsgade

Andersens

Vester Volda

Radhus
pladsen

Rådhus
pladsen

Vesterbro Boulevard

STRØ

Vester

Voldga

Alexandra

Uformel

Trio

Kastanievej

Uranlavej

Østeds

H.C.

Lykkesholms Alle

Fortabnlngsholms
Alle

Segade

Vodroffsvej

Radisson
Blu Royal

Imperial

TIVOLI

Mêlée

Mynstersvej

Alhambravej

Kongevej

Varner-
damsvej

Gammel

Kongevej

Nimb

HOVEDBANE
GÅRD

Bernstorffsgade

Gemys

Frederiksberg

Allé

Vesterbrogade

Westend

Hebron

Reventlows-
gade

Tigh

Vesterbrogade

Danebrogsgade

Andersen

Tietgensgade

Ingerslevs

Tielgensgade
gade

Øl & Brød

Gasværksvej

Istedgade

Absalon

Halmtorvet

VESTERBRO

Pony

A — **B**

▲ Hotel
● Restaurant

14

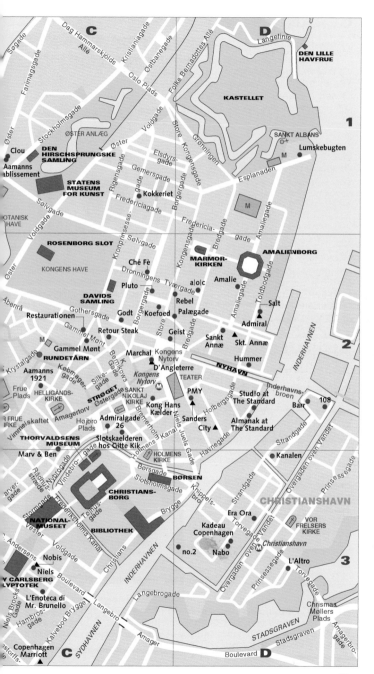

C

Sogade

Farimagsgade

Dag Hammarskjölds Allé

Kristianiagade

Østbanegade

Oslo Plads

Folke Bernadottes Allé

Langelinie

DEN LILLE HAVFRUE

D

KASTELLET

Øster

Stockholmsgade

ØSTER ANLÆG

Øster

Voldgade

Store Kongensgade

Grønningen

SANKT ALBANS

Lumskebugten

M

Clou

DEN HIRSCHSPRUNGSKE SAMLING

Aamanns blissement

Elsdyrs-gade

Gemersgade

Rigensgade

Kokkeriet

Esplanaden

STATENS MUSEUM FOR KUNST

Fredericiagade

M

Fredericia-gade

Amaliegade

OTANISK HAVE

Sølvgade

Voldgade

1

ROSENBORG SLOT

Øster

Kronprinsesse

Sølvgade

Kongensgade

Bredgade

AMALIENBORG

Toldbodgade

MARMOR-KIRKEN

KONGENS HAVE

Ché Fè

Dronningens Tværgade

alolc

Amalie

Amaliegade

Pluto

DAVIDS SAMLING

Borgergade

Rebel

Salt

Gothersgade

Godt

Koefoed

Palægade

Admiral

Restaurationen

Store

Geist

Gammel Mont

Retour Steak

Sankt Annæ

Skt. Annæ

M

Gammel Mønt

Marchal

Kongens Nytorv

Hummer

RUNDETÅRN

Krystalgade

Købmagergade

Barnekows Gade

D'Angleterre

NYHAVN

Inderhavns-broen

INDERHAVNEN

2

Aamanns 1921

Silke-gade

Kongens Nytorv

TEATER

Studio at The Standard

Abenrå

Frue Plads

HELLIGÅNDS-KIRKE

STRØGET

Østergade

SANKT NIKOLAJ KIRKE

PMY

Holbergsgade

Barr

108

R FRUE IRKE

Vimmelskaftet

Amagertorv

Kong Hans Kælder

Niels Juels Gade

Bremerholm

Sanders City

Almanak at The Standard

Strandgade

Gammelskaftet

Højbro Plads

Admiralgade 26

Overgaden oven Vandet

THORVALDSENS MUSEUM

Slotskælderen hos Gitte Kik

Holmens Kanal

Havnegade

Kanalen

Prinsessegade

Marv & Ben

HOLMENS KIRKE

Børsgade

BØRSEN

arver-gade

Stormgade

Nybrogade

Vindebro-gade

Slotsholmsgade

Knippels-bro

CHRISTIANSHAVN

Era Ora

VOR FRELSERS KIRKE

CHRISTIANS-BORG

Brygge

Torvegade

Overgaden oven Vandet

NATIONAL-MUSEET

Vester Voldgade

BIBLIOTHEK

Kadeau Copenhagen

Christianshavn

M

Andersens

Nobis

Christians

no.2

Nabo

Prinsessegade

L'Altro

Torvegade

Niels Brocks Gade

Y CARLSBERG LYPTOTEK

Niels

Boulevard

INDERHAVNEN

Overgaden oven Vandet

3

L'Enoteca di Mr. Brunello

Hambros-gade

Kalvebod Brygge

Langebro

Langebrogade

Amager

Chrismas Møllers Plads

Amagerbro-gade

storfis.

Copenhagen Marriott

C

SYDHAVNEN

Boulevard

STADSGRAVEN

Stadsgraven

D

GERANIUM ✿✿✿

CREATIVE • DESIGN • ELEGANT

Per Henrik Lings Allé 4 (8th Fl), Parken National Stadium (3 km via Dag Hammaraskjölds Allé) ⊠ 2100 Ø
TEL. 69 96 00 20 – **www**.geranium.dk
Closed 2 weeks Christmas, 2 weeks summer and Sunday-Tuesday
Menu 2000 DKK (surprise menu only) (booking essential)

Chef:
Rasmus Kofoed

Specialities:
Lobster, fermented carrot juice & sea buckthorn. Salted hake, parsley stems and caviar in buttermilk. Beeswax and pollen ice cream with rhubarb.

It might be unusually located on the 8th floor of the National Football Stadium, but with its panoramic park views, this luxurious restaurant feels as if it is inviting the outside in. Modern techniques and the finest organic and biodynamic ingredients are used to create beautiful, pure and balanced dishes.

A|O|C ✿✿

MODERN CUISINE • ELEGANT • ROMANTIC

Dronningens Tvaergade 2 ⊠ 1302 K – **PLAN: D2**
Ⓜ Kongens Nytorv
TEL. 33 11 11 45 – **www**.restaurantaoc.dk
Closed Christmas, 1 week February, July, Sunday and Monday
Menu 1500/1800 DKK (dinner only) (tasting menu only)

Chef:
Søren Selin

Specialities:
Onion with caviar and elderflower. Roe deer with ramson butter. Burnt artichoke with hazelnuts and caramel ice cream.

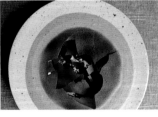

A spacious, simply decorated restaurant in the vaults of an eye-catching 17C building close to Nyhavn harbour; owned and run by an experienced sommelier. Skilful, well-judged and, at times, playful cooking has a Danish heart and shows great originality, as well as a keen eye for detail, flavour and texture.

KADEAU COPENHAGEN ❀❀

MODERN CUISINE • DESIGN • FASHIONABLE   XxX

Wildersgade 10B ⊠ 1408 K – **PLAN: D3**
Ⓜ Christianshavn
TEL. 33 25 22 23 – **www**.kadeau.dk
Closed 5 weeks July-August, 1 week Christmas and Sunday-Tuesday
Menu 1850 DKK (dinner only and Saturday lunch)
(tasting menu only) (booking essential)

Chef:
Nicolai Nørregaard
Specialities:
Garden vegetable terrine with tomato broth and cherry oil. Peas with mint and roasted nasturtium. Smoked celeriac, white asparagus and woodruff.

You'll receive a warm welcome at this delightful restaurant, where the open kitchen adds a sense of occasion to the sophisticated room. The chefs have an innate understanding of how best to match fresh and aged produce, and use their experience in preserving and fermenting to add many elements to each dish.

CLOU ❀

MODERN CUISINE • INTIMATE • NEIGHBOURHOOD   XX

Øster Farimagsgade 8 ⊠ 2100 K – **PLAN: C1**
Ⓜ Nørreport
TEL. 91 92 72 30 – **www**.restaurant-clou.dk
Closed Sunday-Tuesday
Menu 1600 DKK (dinner only) (tasting menu only)
(booking essential)

Chef:
Jonathan Berntsen
Specialities:
Sea urchin and Oscietra caviar. Boudin noir with truffle and blackcurrant. Pickled fruits and cow's milk sorbet.

An intimate, suburban restaurant where you can see into the basement kitchen from the street. The tasting 'journey' of 20 dishes is designed to match 6 carefully chosen, top quality wines. Creative dishes stimulate the senses with their intense natural flavours and well-balanced contrasts in texture and taste.

Marie Louise Munkegaard/Kadeau • Michelin

ERA ORA ❀

ITALIAN • ELEGANT • INTIMATE

XxX ❀ 🏠

Overgaden Neden Vandet 33B ⊠ 1414 K – PLAN: D3
🅜 Christianshavn
TEL. 32 54 06 93 – **www**.era-ora.dk
Closed 24-26 December, 1 January, Easter Monday and Sunday

Menu 598/1250 DKK (tasting menu only) (booking essential)

Specialities:
Pasta with porcini and hazelnuts.
Braised beef cheek, potato purée
and dragon kale. Sweet plin ravioli,
black tea and orange broth.

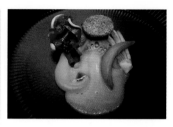

Set on a quaint cobbled street by the canal, a grand, long-standing
restaurant with an enclosed rear terrace and a formal air. Complex,
innovative dishes feature lots of different ingredients (many imported
from Italy) and are often explorative in their approach. The wine cellar
boasts over 90,000 bottles.

FORMEL B ❀

MODERN CUISINE • FASHIONABLE • DESIGN

XX ❀ A/C

Vesterbrogade 182-184, Frederiksberg (2 km on
Vesterbrogade) ⊠ 1800 C
TEL. 33 25 10 66 – **www**.formelb.dk
Closed 24-26 December and Sunday

Menu 850 DKK – Carte 615/895 DKK (dinner only)
(booking essential)

Chef:
Kristian Arpe-Møller

Specialities:
Langoustine à la nage with Danish
vegetables. Sweetbread, kale,
rhubarb, horseradish and acidified
cream. Sea buckthorn 'en surprise'.

The friendly staff help to create a relaxed environment at this
appealing modern restaurant, with its tree pictures and dark wood
branches; ask for a table on the lower level by the kitchen if you want
to get close to the action. Complex, original small plates are crafted
with an assured and confident touch.

KIIN KIIN ❀

THAI • EXOTIC DÉCOR • INTIMATE

Guldbergsgade 21 ✉ 2200 N – **PLAN: A1**
TEL. 35 35 75 55 – **www**.kiin.dk
Closed Christmas and Sunday

Menu 495/975 DKK (dinner only) (tasting menu only)
(booking essential)

Specialities:
Frozen red curry with baby lobster and coriander. Quail in coconut milk with lemongrass. Lemon and lime foam with holy basil sorbet.

A charming restaurant, whose name means 'come and eat'. Start with refined versions of street food in the moody lounge, then head for the tasteful dining room decorated with golden Buddhas and fresh flowers. Menus offer modern, personal interpretations of Thai dishes, which have vibrant flavour combinations.

KOKKERIET ❀

MODERN CUISINE • INTIMATE • DESIGN

Kronprinsessegade 64 ✉ 1306 K – **PLAN: C1**
TEL. 33 15 27 77 – **www**.kokkeriet.dk
Closed 24-26 December, 1 January and Sunday

Menu 900/1200 DKK (dinner only) (tasting menu only)
(booking essential)

Specialities:
Scallops, green strawberries, almonds and mussel sauce. Quail with squid tart, garlic and parsley. Ice cream with apple, and brown sugar sauce.

A discreet, elegant corner restaurant with two narrow, atmospheric rooms decorated in black and grey and hung with a collection of contemporary art. Modern dishes keep their focus firmly on nature, while the traditional Danish flavours will evoke memories of childhood; the midweek 'test' menus are good value.

Kiin Kiin • Kokkeriet

KONG HANS KÆLDER ⌘

CLASSIC FRENCH • ELEGANT • INTIMATE   XxX ⌘ ⌑

Vingaardsstræde 6 ⊠ 1070 K – PLAN: C2
Ⓜ Kongens Nytorv
TEL. 33 11 68 68 – **www**.konghans.dk
Closed 13-27 February, 11-12 April, 24 July-14 August, 24-28
December, 31 December and Sunday-Tuesday

Menu 1700 DKK – Carte 1115/2215 DKK (dinner only)
(booking essential)

Specialities:
Turbot with olive blanquette and
black truffle. Black lobster 'à
la nage', 'thermidor' and 'à
l'américaine'. Chocolate soufflé
and vanilla ice cream.

An intimate, historic restaurant in a beautiful vaulted Gothic cellar
in the heart of the city. Richly flavoured, classic French cooking uses
luxury ingredients – signature dishes could include Danish Black
lobster. There's a 5 course tasting menu and Gueridon trolleys add a
theatrical element to proceedings.

MARCHAL ⌘

MODERN CUISINE • ELEGANT • ROMANTIC   XX ⌘ & 🏠 AC

D'Angleterre Hotel • Kongens Nytorv 34 ⊠ 1050 K – PLAN: C2
Ⓜ Kongens Nytorv
TEL. 33 12 00 94 – **www**.marchal.dk
Menu 525 DKK (lunch) – Carte 585/1185 DKK

Specialities:
Squid with oysters, caviar and
champagne butter. Chateaubriand,
smoked marrow and pepper sauce.
"Gold Bar" with hazelnuts and
calvados ice cream.

A stylish hotel restaurant overlooking the Square and named after
the man who founded the hotel in 1755. Refined, Nordic-style cooking
has a classical French base; menus offer a range of small plates – 3
is about the right amount. Dinner also includes an extensive caviar
collection.

Michelin • Michelin

108 ✿

MODERN CUISINE • NEIGHBOURHOOD • DESIGN

Strandgade 108 ✉ 1401 K - **PLAN: D2**
Ⓜ Christianshavn
TEL. 32 96 32 92 – **www**.108.dk
Closed Christmas and 1 January

Carte 405/970 DKK (dinner only) (booking advisable)

Chef:
Kristian Baumann
Specialities:
Courgette flowers and summer greens. Glazed pork belly with salted apples. Rose hips with sea buckthorn.

A former whale meat warehouse with floor-to-ceiling windows and water views; bare concrete and a semi-open kitchen give it a cool Nordic style. There's a Noma alumnus in the kitchen and plenty of pickled, cured and fermented ingredients on the 'no rules' menu, from which you pick as many dishes as you like.

RELÆ ✿

MODERN CUISINE • MINIMALIST • FASHIONABLE

Jægersborggade 41 ✉ 2200 N - **PLAN: A1**
TEL. 36 96 66 09 – **www**.restaurant-relae.dk
Closed Christmas-New Year, Sunday and Monday

Menu 475/895 DKK (dinner only and lunch Friday- Saturday) (surprise menu only) (booking essential)

Specialities:
Green strawberries and marigold. Havervadgård lamb, romaine salad and tarragon. Yoghurt, chervil and lemon.

This modern, understated restaurant never stands still. The open kitchen provides a real sense of occasion and you can feel the passion of the chefs as they explain the dishes they are serving. 5 and 10 course surprise menus showcase produce grown on their farm. Dishes are intensely flavoured and unrestrained.

STUD!O AT THE STANDARD ✿

CREATIVE • FASHIONABLE • DESIGN   ✗✗ ≼ A/C

Havnegade 44 ⊠ 1058 K – PLAN: D2
Ⓜ Kongens Nytorv
TEL. 72 14 88 08 – **www**.thestandardcph.dk
Closed 8-30 July, 23 December-3 January, 17-25
February, Sunday and Monday

Menu 1300 DKK (dinner only and Saturday lunch)
(surprise menu only) (booking essential)

Specialities:
Pike ceviche with sweet onion and
whitecurrant. Duck with grapes and
lavender. Almond ice cream, cep
and balsamico.

The action at this stylishly understated restaurant is focused around
the open kitchen, with seating of varying heights so everyone has a
view. You'll notice subtle references to Chile – the chef's homeland – in
the 7 course surprise menu. Precisely prepared, intensely flavoured
dishes are full of creativity.

L'ALTRO ☻

ITALIAN • INTIMATE • TRADITIONAL DÉCOR   ✗ A/C

Torvegade 62 ⊠ 1400 K – PLAN: D3
Ⓜ Christianshavn
TEL. 32 54 54 06 – **www**.laltro.dk
Closed Easter, 1-15 January, Tuesday and Wednesday

Menu 340/450 DKK (dinner only) (tasting menu only)
(booking essential)

A cosy, long-standing restaurant with a warm, rustic style; it
celebrates 'la cucina de la casa' – the homely Italian spirit of "mama's
kitchen". Regularly changing set menus feature tasty family recipes
from Umbria and Tuscany; dishes are appealing and rely on good
quality ingredients imported from Italy.

ANARKI 🐼

TRADITIONAL CUISINE • NEIGHBOURHOOD • BISTRO

Vodroffsvej 47 ⊠ 1900 C – PLAN: A2
🚇 Forum
TEL. 22 13 11 34 – **www**.restaurant-anarki.dk
Closed July, Christmas, Easter and Monday
Menu 395 DKK – Carte 275/435 DKK (dinner only)

An unassuming and proudly run neighbourhood bistro, set just over the water in Frederiksberg. The interesting menu of gutsy, flavourful dishes draws inspiration from all over the world, so expect to see words like ceviche, paella and burrata as well as bakskuld – with plenty of offal and some great wines.

ENOMANIA 🐼

ITALIAN • WINE BAR • SIMPLE

Vesterbrogade 187 (2.5 km via Vesterbrogade) ⊠ 1800 C
TEL. 33 23 60 80 – **www**.enomania.dk
Closed 22 December-2 January, 9-18 February, 29 March-2 April, 18-22 April, 7 July-6 August, 13-22 October, Saturday-Monday and bank holidays
Menu 390 DKK – Carte 260/380 DKK (dinner only and lunch Thursday-Friday) (booking essential)

A simple, bistro-style restaurant near Frederiksberg Park – its name means 'Wine Mania'. The wine cellar comes with a table for tasting and there's an excellent list of over 600 bins, mostly from Piedmont and Burgundy. These are complemented by straightforward, tasty Italian dishes from a daily 4 course menu.

FREDERIKS HAVE 😊

DANISH • NEIGHBOURHOOD • FAMILY   XX 🏠

Smallegade 41, (entrance on Virginiavej) (1.5 km. via Gammel
Kongevej) ✉ 2000 F
Ⓜ Frederiksberg
TEL. 38 88 33 35 – **www**.frederikshave.dk
Closed 24 December-1 January, Easter and Sunday
Menu 295/535 DKK – Carte 340/530 DKK

A sweet neighbourhood restaurant hidden just off the main street in
a residential area. Sit inside – surrounded by flowers and vivid local
art – or outside, on the terrace. Well-presented, modern Danish dishes
have a classical base; tasty sweet and sour combinations feature. The
set lunches are great value.

KØDBYENS FISKEBAR 😊

SEAFOOD • SIMPLE • FASHIONABLE   X 🏠 P

Den Hvide Kødby, Flæsketorvet 100 (1 km via Halmtorvet) ✉ 1711 V
TEL. 32 15 56 56 – **www**.fiskebaren.dk
Closed 24-26 December and lunch Monday to Thursday
Menu 295 DKK (lunch) – Carte 290/565 DKK

 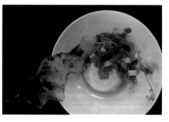

This buzzy, industrial-style restaurant is set, somewhat incongruously,
in a former butcher's shop in a commercial meat market. Menus
feature freshly prepared 'hot' and 'cold' seafood dishes which are
based around the latest catch and oysters are a speciality. The terrace
is a popular spot come summer.

MARV & BEN ⊛

MODERN CUISINE • FRIENDLY • ROMANTIC   ✗

Snaregade 4 ⊠ 1205 K – PLAN: C2/3
Ⓜ Kongens Nytorv
TEL. 33 91 01 91 – **www**.marvogben.dk
Closed Christmas and Sunday

Menu 400/600 DKK – Carte 305/355 DKK (dinner only)
(booking advisable)

The young owners bring plenty of enthusiasm to this little restaurant, where dining is split over two dimly lit floors. Organic produce features in seasonal dishes which display purity and depth of flavour. Choose 'Four Favourites' (4 courses), 'Almost Everything' (6 courses) or from the à la carte.

MÊLÉE ⊛

FRENCH • FRIENDLY • BISTRO   ✗

Martensens Allé 16 ⊠ 1828 C – PLAN: A3
Ⓜ Frederiksberg
TEL. 35 13 11 34 – **www**.melee.dk
Closed Christmas-New Year, Easter and Sunday

Menu 395 DKK – Carte 325/430 DKK (dinner only)
(booking essential)

A bustling neighbourhood bistro with a friendly, laid-back atmosphere; run by an experienced team. Modern, country-style cooking is French-based but has Danish influences; menus might be concise but portions are generous and flavours are bold. An excellent range of wines from the Rhône Valley accompany.

MUSLING BISTRO 🌢

SEAFOOD • BISTRO • FASHIONABLE　　　　　🍴 AC

Linnésgade 14 ✉ 1361 K – PLAN: B1
TEL. 34 10 56 56 – **www**.musling.net
Closed 24-25 December, Sunday and Monday

Carte 360/480 DKK

A relaxed bar-cum-bistro next to the Nørrebro food market – find a
space at the black ash counter, grab your cutlery from one of the pots,
and choose from the list of modern craft beers and unusual wines.
Fantastic fresh seafood is to the fore on the concise menu, and service
is swift and efficient.

PLUTO 🌢

MEDITERRANEAN CUISINE • BISTRO • RUSTIC　　🍴 🏠

Borgergade 16 ✉ 1300 K – PLAN: C2
Ⓜ Kongens Nytorv
TEL. 33 16 00 16 – **www**.restaurantpluto.dk
Closed 24-25 December and 1 January

Menu 475 DKK – Carte 235/410 DKK (dinner only)

An appealing restaurant in a residential area, with concrete pillars and
an intentionally 'unfinished' feel – sit at wooden tables, at the long
metal bar or at communal marble-topped tables. An enticing menu of
small plates includes 'cheese' and 'sweets' sections; cooking is rustic,
unfussy and flavoursome.

PMY 🏠

SOUTH AMERICAN • FRIENDLY • TRENDY

Tordenskjoldsgade 11 ✉ 1055 K – PLAN: D2
Ⓜ Kongens Nytorv
TEL. 50 81 00 02 – **www**.restaurant-pmy.com
Closed July, Christmas, 1 week January, Monday and Tuesday
Menu 375/495 DKK (dinner only) (booking essential)

Start with some snacks and a cocktail at this fun, laid-back restaurant, before moving on to fresh, zingy dishes bursting with Latin American flavours. Potato, maize and yuca feature highly on the small menu, which lists tasty, good value dishes from Peru, Mexico and Venezuela.

REBEL 🏠

MODERN CUISINE • BISTRO • FASHIONABLE

Store Kongensgade 52 ✉ 1264 K – PLAN: C/D2
Ⓜ Kongens Nytorv
TEL. 33 32 32 09 – **www**.restaurantrebel.dk
Closed 23 July-6 August, 2 weeks Christmas, Sunday and Monday
Carte 335/565 DKK (dinner only)

Located in a busy part of the city; a simply decorated, split-level restaurant with closely set tables and a buzzy vibe. Choose 3 or 4 dishes from the list of 12 starter-sized options; cooking is modern and refined, and relies largely on Danish produce. The atmospheric lower floor is often used for parties.

AAMANNS ETABLISSEMENT ⅈ○

DANISH • BISTRO • COSY

Øster Farimagsgade 12 ✉ 2100 Ø – PLAN: C1
Ⓜ Nørreport
TEL. 20 80 52 02 – **www**.aamanns.dk
Closed July, Christmas-New Year and dinner Sunday-Tuesday
Carte 325/460 DKK (booking advisable)

A cosy, contemporary restaurant with cheery service and an informal
atmosphere. Concise, seasonal menus blend traditional smørrebrød
with more modern 'small plates'. Two dishes per person plus dessert
is about right.

AAMANNS 1921 ⅈ○

MODERN CUISINE • BRASSERIE • DESIGN

Niels Hemmingsens Gade 19-21 ✉ 1153 K – PLAN: C2
Ⓜ Kongens Nytorv
TEL. 20 80 52 04 – **www**.aamanns.dk
Closed 25-26 December, 31 December, 1 January and dinner
Sunday-Monday
Menu 325/390 DKK – Carte 265/475 DKK (booking advisable)

An appealing restaurant with original stone arches. Lunch sees
traditional smørrebrød, while dinner focuses on modern dishes. They
grind and mill their own flours, marinate their herring for 6-12 months
and gather the herbs for their snaps.

ADMIRALGADE 26 🍴

MODERN CUISINE • INTIMATE • COSY

Admiralgade 26 ✉ 1066 K – **PLAN: C2**
Ⓜ Kongens Nytorv
TEL. 33 33 79 73 – **www**.admiralgade26.dk
Closed Christmas, 31 December-2 January and Sunday

Menu 550 DKK – Carte 305/425 DKK

This historic house dates from 1796 and sits in one of the oldest parts of the city. It's a relaxed place – a mix of wine bar, café and bistro – and, alongside an appealing modern menu, offers around 4,000 frequently changing wines.

ALMANAK AT THE STANDARD 🍴

MODERN CUISINE • FASHIONABLE • CHIC

Havnegade 44 ✉ 1058 K – **PLAN: D2**
Ⓜ Kongens Nytorv
TEL. 72 14 88 08 – **www**.thestandardcph.dk
Closed 24-25 December and Monday

Menu 575 DKK (dinner) – Carte 265/500 DKK
(bookings advisable at dinner)

A chic restaurant on the ground floor of an impressive art deco customs building on the waterfront. At lunch, it's all about smørrebrød, while dinner sees a concise menu of updated Danish classics. An open kitchen adds to the theatre.

AMALIE ⅋⅋

SMØRREBRØD • INTIMATE • RUSTIC

Amaliegade 11 ✉ 1256 K – PLAN: D2
Ⓜ Kongens Nytorv
TEL. 33 12 88 10 – **www**.restaurantamalie.dk
Closed 3 weeks July, 24 December-3 January, Easter, Sunday and bank holidays
Menu 279 DKK – Carte 230/350 DKK (lunch only)
(booking essential)

Charming 18C townhouse by Amalienborg Palace, with two tiny, cosy rooms filled with old paintings and elegant porcelain. The Danish menu offers a large choice of smørrebrød, herring, salmon and salads. Service is warm and welcoming.

AMASS ⅋⅋

DANISH • MINIMALIST • FRIENDLY

Refshalevej 153 (3 km via Torvgade and Prinsessgade) ✉ 1432 K
TEL. 43 58 43 30 – **www**.amassrestaurant.com
Closed 1 week Summer, Christmas, February, Sunday and Monday
Menu 695/895 DKK (dinner only and lunch Friday-Saturday)
(booking essential)

A large restaurant just outside the city. It has an urban, industrial feel courtesy of graffitied concrete walls and huge windows overlooking the old docks. Prices and the authenticity of ingredients are key; cooking is modern Danish.

BARR ⚫

MODERN CUISINE • TRENDY • RUSTIC

Strandgade 93 ⊠ 1401 K – **PLAN: D2**
Ⓜ Christianshavn
TEL. 32 96 32 93 – **www**.restaurantbarr.com
Closed 1 November and 22 December-3 January
Carte 325/455 DKK (dinner only and lunch Friday-Sunday)
(booking essential)

A laid-back quayside restaurant with wood-clad walls. Its name means
'Barley' and it offers an amazing array of cask and bottled beers –
some custom-brewed – and beer pairings to match the food. Intensely
flavoured, rustic dishes have classic Nordic roots but are taken to new
heights; the sweet cake is a must.

BRACE ⚫

ITALIAN • ELEGANT • FASHIONABLE

Teglgårdstræde 8a ⊠ 1452 K – **PLAN: B2**
Ⓜ København Hovedbane Gård
TEL. 28 88 20 01 – **www**.restaurantbrace.dk
Closed 24-26 December, 2-22 January, Sunday and Monday
Menu 350/775 DKK (dinner only) (booking essential)

The name of this smart restaurant, set in the heart of the city, refers
to the building's external structure and to the solidarity of the tight-
knit team. Dishes are a fusion of Danish and Italian, and come with
colourful modern twists.

Line Klein/Barr • Nicolai Amter/Barr • Nikolai Linares and Luka Donninelli/Brace - Nikolai Linares and Luka Donninelli/Brace

CHÉ FÈ ⅈ○

ITALIAN • SIMPLE • NEIGHBOURHOOD ⅹ

Borgergade 17a ✉ 1300 K – **PLAN: C2**
Ⓜ Kongens Nytorv
TEL. 33 11 17 21 – **www**.chefe.dk
Closed 1 week Christmas, 1 January and Sunday

Menu 385/495 DKK – Carte 425/485 DKK (dinner only)
(booking essential)

An unassuming façade conceals an appealing trattoria with pastel
hues and coffee sack curtains. Menus offer authentic Italian classics,
including homemade pastas; virtually all ingredients are imported
from small, organic producers.

L' ENOTECA DI MR. BRUNELLO ⅈ○

ITALIAN • ELEGANT • NEIGHBOURHOOD ⅹⅹ ❀

Rysensteensgade 16 ✉ 1564 K – **PLAN: C3**
TEL. 33 11 47 20 – **www**.lenoteca.dk
Closed Easter, 1 July-8 August, 23 December-2 January, Sunday and
bank holidays

Menu 495/695 DKK – Carte 530/560 DKK (dinner only)

Tucked away near the Tivoli Gardens and run by passionate,
experienced owners. Refined, classic Italian cooking uses good
quality produce imported from Italy. The good value Italian wine
list has over 150 different Brunello di Montalcinos.

56° ⑩

DANISH • RUSTIC • ROMANTIC ✗ 🏠 ⇩

Krudtløbsvej 8 (2.5 km. via Torvgade, Prinsessgade and
Refshalevej) ✉ 1439 K
TEL. 31 16 32 05 – **www**.restaurant56grader.dk
Closed Christmas, lunch Tuesday-Thursday in winter, Sunday dinner
and Monday

Menu 275/400 DKK

A sweet, rustic restaurant, unusually set within the 1.5m thick walls of
a 17C gunpowder store. Flavoursome Danish cooking mixes modern
and traditional elements and keeps Nordic produce to the fore. The
large garden is a hit.

GAMMEL MØNT ⑩

TRADITIONAL CUISINE • COSY • FRIENDLY ✗✗

Gammel Mønt 41 ✉ 1117 K – **PLAN: C2**
Ⓜ Kongens Nytorv
TEL. 33 15 10 60 – **www**.glmoent.dk
Closed July, Christmas, Easter, Sunday, Monday and bank holidays

Carte 455/685 DKK (lunch only and dinner Wednesday-Friday)

A part-timbered house in the heart of the city; it dates back to 1739
and sports a striking shade of deep terracotta. The menu celebrates
Danish flavours and dishes are gutsy and reassuringly traditional – try
the pickled herrings.

GEIST ❧○

MODERN CUISINE • DESIGN • TRENDY ✕✕ 🏠 AK

Kongens Nytorv 8 ✉ 1050 K – **PLAN: C2**
Ⓜ Kongens Nytorv
TEL. 33 13 37 13 – **www**.restaurantgeist.dk
Closed 23-26 December and 1 January
Carte 385/840 DKK (dinner only)

A lively, fashionable restaurant with an open kitchen and a sexy nightclub vibe, set in a striking red-brick property with floor to ceiling windows overlooking the square. Cleverly crafted dishes display a light touch; 4 should suffice.

GEMYSE ❧○

MODERN CUISINE • RUSTIC • ROMANTIC ✕ 🏠 ❖

Nimb Hotel • Tivoli Gardens, Bernstoffsgade 5 ✉ 1572 V – **PLAN: B3**
Ⓜ København Hovedbane Gård
TEL. 88 70 00 80 – **www**.nimb.dk
Menu 250/600 DKK – Carte 215/275 DKK

Part of the Nimb hotel, Gemyse is a delightful, vegetable-orientated restaurant set in the heart of Tivoli Gardens, and comes complete with a greenhouse and raised beds where they grow much of their produce. Dishes are well-prepared, attractively presented and very tasty. The daily set menu is a good choice.

Restaurant Geist - Restaurant Geist • Lina Ahnoff and Rasmus Palsgård/Gemyse • Lina Ahnoff and Rasmus Palsgård/Gemyse

GODT ⦙○

CLASSIC CUISINE • FRIENDLY • FAMILY   XX

Gothersgade 38 ✉ 1123 K – **PLAN: C2**
Ⓜ Kongens Nytorv
TEL. 33 15 21 22 – **www**.restaurant-godt.dk
Closed mid July to mid August, Christmas-New Year, Easter,
Sunday, Monday and bank holidays
Menu 600/680 DKK (dinner only) (tasting menu only)

 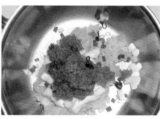

A stylish restaurant seating just 20; the service here is particularly
friendly. Traditional French and European daily menus – of 4 and 5
courses – are formed around the latest market produce. Old WWII
shells act as candle holders.

GORILLA ⦙○

MODERN CUISINE • BRASSERIE • SIMPLE   X 🏠

Flæsketorvet 63 (1 km via Halmtorvet) ✉ 1711 V
TEL. 33 33 83 30 – **www**.restaurantgorilla.dk
Closed 24-25 December, 1 January, Sunday and bank holidays
Menu 375/475 DKK – Carte 135/860 DKK (dinner only)

A buzzy, canteen-style restaurant in the meatpacking district; the
stone floor, zinc ducting and large windows create an industrial feel.
The menu offers something for everyone; dishes are well-presented,
tasty and designed for sharing.

HÖST ⁞○

MODERN CUISINE • FRIENDLY • RUSTIC

Nørre Farimagsgade 41 ✉ 1364 K – **PLAN: B2**
Ⓜ Nørreport
TEL. 89 93 84 09 – **www**.cofoco.dk/restauranter/hoest
Closed 24 December, 1 January and lunch Sunday-Wednesday
Menu 350/895 DKK

A busy neighbourhood bistro with fun staff and a lively atmosphere; sit in the Garden Room. The great value monthly set menu comprises 3 courses but comes with lots of extras. Modern Nordic cooking is seasonal and boldly flavoured.

HUMMER ⁞○

SEAFOOD • FRIENDLY • SIMPLE

Nyhavn 63A ✉ 1051 K – **PLAN: D2**
Ⓜ Kongens Nytorv
TEL. 33 33 03 39 – **www**.restauranthummer.dk
Closed 23-27 December and Monday-Tuesday October-April
Menu 395 DKK – Carte 280/610 DKK

Lobster is the mainstay of the menu at this restaurant, situated among the brightly coloured buildings on the famous Nyhavn strip. Enjoy a meal on the sunny terrace or in the modish, nautically styled dining room.

KANALEN ⑩

DANISH • BISTRO • COSY

Wilders Plads 1-3 ✉ 1403 K – **PLAN: D3**
Ⓜ Christianshavn
TEL. 32 95 13 30 – **www**.restaurant-kanalen.dk
Closed Christmas, New Years Eve, Easter, Sunday and bank holidays
Menu 300/400 DKK – Carte 335/555 DKK (booking essential)

Find a spot on the delightful canalside terrace of this quaint, shack-like building – formerly the Harbour Police office – and watch the boats bobbing up and down as you eat. Alongside classic Danish flavours you'll find some light French and Asian touches; for dessert, the 'flødeboller' is a must.

KIIN KIIN VEVE ⑩

VEGETARIAN • DESIGN • CONTEMPORARY DÉCOR ✗✗

Dampfærgevej 7-9 (North 2.5 km by Store Kongensgade and Folke Bernadottes Allé) ✉ 2100 Ø
TEL. 51 22 59 55 – **www**.veve.dk
Closed Sunday-Tuesday
Menu 750 DKK (dinner only) (tasting menu only) (booking essential)

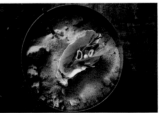

A former bread factory houses this chic restaurant which serves sophisticated vegetarian cuisine. The 6 course tasting menu revolves around the seasons and offers some imaginative combinations. Wine and juice pairings accompany.

KOEFOED 🍴

MODERN CUISINE • INTIMATE • ROMANTIC   XX 🕸 🏠

Landgreven 3 ✉ 1301 K – PLAN: C2
Ⓜ Kongens Nytorv
TEL. 56 48 22 24 – **www**.restaurant-koefoed.dk
Closed 22 December-4 January and Sunday-Tuesday

Menu 295/495 DKK – Carte 425/510 DKK
(booking essential at dinner)

An intimate collection of rooms in an old coal cellar, where everything
from the produce to the glassware celebrates Bornholm island.
Modern cooking is accompanied by an impressive range of bordeaux
wines. Lunch sees reinvented smørrebrød.

LUMSKEBUGTEN 🍴

TRADITIONAL CUISINE • COSY • CLASSIC DÉCOR   XX 🏠 ⬭

Esplanaden 21 ✉ 1263 K – PLAN: D1
TEL. 33 15 60 29 – **www**.lumskebugten.dk
Closed 3 weeks July, Christmas, Easter, Sunday and bank holidays
Menu 325/475 DKK – Carte 450/700 DKK

A restored quayside pavilion dating from 1854; the Royal Family
occasionally dine here. A series of small rooms are adorned with
maritime memorabilia and paintings. Local menus offer a wide
selection of traditional fish dishes.

MES ❧

DANISH • INTIMATE • FRIENDLY

Jarmers Plads 1 ✉ 1551 V – **PLAN: B2**
Ⓜ København Hovedbane Gård
TEL. 25 36 51 81 – **www**.restaurant-mes.dk
Closed 24-30 December and Sunday

Menu 350 DKK (dinner only) (tasting menu only)
(booking essential)

A sweet little restaurant run by a tight-knit team. The frequently
changing set menu lists classic dishes – some of which are pepped
up with modern techniques. A 120 year old German cooling cabinet
plays host to the wines.

MIELCKE & HURTIGKARL ❧

CREATIVE • ELEGANT • EXOTIC DÉCOR

Runddel 1 (2 km via Veseterbrogade and Frederiksberg
Allé) ✉ 2000 C
TEL. 38 34 84 36 – **www**.mhcph.com
Closed 3 weeks Christmas, Sunday and Monday

Menu 800/1100 DKK (dinner only) (booking essential)

A charming 1744 orangery with a fire-lit terrace, set in a delightful
spot in Frederiksberg Gardens. The walls are painted with garden
scenes and dishes use an amazing array of herbs which come from the
garden. Dishes originate from around the globe but Asian influences
are kept to the fore.

NABO ⅋○

DANISH • COSY • NEIGHBOURHOOD

Wildersgade 10a ✉ 1408 K – **PLAN: D3**
Ⓜ Christianhavn
TEL. 33 22 10 02 – **www**.nabonabo.dk
Closed Christmas, Monday dinner and Sunday

Carte 320/435 DKK

This laid-back restaurant – sister to neighbouring Kadeau – is open from morning 'til night, for everything from coffee to a 3 course meal. Sit surrounded by preserving jars and Danish pottery. The rustic cooking really hits the spot.

NIELS ⅋○

MODERN CUISINE • DESIGN • CHIC

Nobis Hotel • Niels Brocks Gade 1 ✉ 1574 V – **PLAN: C3**
Ⓜ København Hovedbane Gård
TEL. 78 74 14 00 – **www**.nobishotel.dk

Menu 200/645 DKK – Carte 515/755 DKK

Lots of glass and mirrors give this contemporary hotel restaurant an airy feel. Well-presented, satisfying modern Scandinavian cooking gives a nod to France and has plenty of texture and flavour contrasts. In summer, head for the terrace.

NO.2 ☆○

MODERN CUISINE • DESIGN • FASHIONABLE ✗ ⪕ 🏠 AC

Nicolai Eigtveds Gade 32 ✉ 1402 C – PLAN: D3
Ⓜ Christianshaven
TEL. 33 11 11 68 – **www**.nummer2.dk
Closed Christmas, Easter, 2 weeks in July, Saturday lunch and
Sunday
Menu 325/475 DKK – Carte 275/525 DKK

Set among smart offices and apartments on the edge of the dock is
this elegant restaurant; a sister to a|o|c. Fresh, flavoursome dishes
focus on quality Danish ingredients – highlights include the cured
hams, cheeses and ice creams.

ØL & BRØD ☆○

MODERN CUISINE • NEIGHBOURHOOD • COSY   ✗

Viktoriagade 6 ✉ 1620 V – PLAN: B3
Ⓜ København Hovedbane Gård
TEL. 33 31 44 22 – **www**.ologbrod.com
Closed Monday and dinner Tuesday-Wednesday
Menu 500 DKK (dinner) – Carte lunch 280/440 DKK
(booking essential)

A cosy, hip neighbourhood restaurant where the emphasis is as much
on aquavit and craft beers as it is on the refined and flavourful modern
food. Lunch sees smørrebrød taken to a new level, while dinner offers
a choice of 3 or 6 courses.

PALÆGADE ⅋○

SMØRREBRØD • FRIENDLY • SIMPLE   ✗✗ 🛖

Palægade 8 ✉ 1261 K – PLAN: C/D2
Ⓜ Kongens Nytorv
TEL. 70 82 82 88 – **www**.palaegade.dk
Closed 24-27 December, 1 week January, dinner 16 July-5 August
and Sunday dinner
Menu 495 DKK – Carte 285/620 DKK

More than 40 classic smørrebrød are available at lunch – with plenty
of local beers and snaps to accompany them. Things become more
formal in the evenings, when they serve highly seasonal dishes in a
traditional Northern European style.

PONY ⅋○

DANISH • BISTRO • NEIGHBOURHOOD   ✗

Vesterbrogade 135 ✉ 1620 V – PLAN: A3
TEL. 33 22 10 00 – **www**.ponykbh.dk
Closed July-August, 1 week Christmas and Monday
Menu 425/485 DKK (dinner only) (booking essential)

A buzzy restaurant with chatty service: sit on high stools by the
kitchen or in the retro dining room. Choose from the fixed price menu
or try the more adventurous 4 course 'Pony Kick'. Refined, modern
cooking has a 'nose-to-tail' approach.

RADIO ⭐🍴

MODERN CUISINE • MINIMALIST • NEIGHBOURHOOD   ✗

Julius Thomsens Gade 12 ✉ 1632 V – PLAN: A2
Ⓜ Forum
TEL. 25 10 27 33 – **www**.restaurantradio.dk
Closed 3 weeks summer, 2 weeks Christmas-New Year, Sunday and
Monday

Menu 350/435 DKK (dinner only and lunch Friday-Saturday)
(tasting menu only) (booking essential)

An informal restaurant with an unfussy urban style, wood-clad walls
and cool anglepoise lighting. Oft-changing set menus feature full-
flavoured, good value dishes and use organic ingredients grown in
the chefs' nearby fields.

RESTAURATIONEN 🍴

CLASSIC CUISINE • CHIC • ROMANTIC   ✗✗ 🐾

Møntergade 19 ✉ 1116 K – PLAN: C2
Ⓜ Kongens Nytorv
TEL. 33 14 94 95 – **www**.restaurationen.com
Closed July-28 August, 22 December-8 January, 25 March-2 April,
Sunday and Monday

Menu 605 DKK (dinner only)

This restaurant celebrated 25 years in 2016, and is run by a well-known
chef who also owns the next door wine bar. Modern Danish dishes are
created with quality local produce. The dining room displays some
impressive vibrant modern art.

RETOUR STEAK ⅰ○

MEATS AND GRILLS • BISTRO • FRIENDLY ⅹ

Ny Østergade 21 ⊠ 1101 K – **PLAN: C2**
Ⓜ Kongens Nytorv
TEL. 33 16 17 19 – **www**.retoursteak.dk
Closed 24-25 December and 1 January

Carte 240/595 DKK (dinner only) (booking essential)

A relaxed, informal restaurant with a stark white interior and contrasting black furnishings. A small menu offers simply prepared grills, good quality American rib-eye steaks and an affordable selection of wines.

SALT ⅰ○

MODERN CUISINE • DESIGN • FASHIONABLE ⅩⅩ ☂ 🅿

Admiral Hotel • Toldbodgade 24-28 ⊠ 1253 K – **PLAN: D2**
Ⓜ Kongens Nytorv
TEL. 33 74 14 44 – **www**.salt.dk

Menu 395/445 DKK – Carte 430/540 DKK

 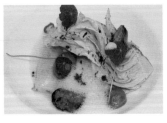

A bright, airy hotel restaurant; its vast old timber beams are a reminder of the building's previous life as a granary and its harbourside terrace is a great spot in the summer. Extensive menus offer interesting modern cooking.

SANKT ANNÆ ⭐🍴

SMØRREBRØD • COSY • CLASSIC DÉCOR

Sankt Annæ Plads 12 ✉ 1250 K – **PLAN: D2**
Ⓜ Kongens Nytorv
TEL. 33 12 54 97 – **www**.restaurantsanktannae.dk
Closed July-August, Sunday and bank holidays
Carte 220/395 DKK (lunch only) (booking essential)

An attractive terraced building with a traditional, rather quaint interior. There's a seasonal à la carte and a daily blackboard menu: prices can vary so check before ordering. The lobster and shrimp – fresh from local fjords – are a hit.

SLOTSKÆLDEREN HOS GITTE KIK 🍴

SMØRREBRØD • FAMILY • TRADITIONAL DÉCOR

Fortunstræde 4 ✉ 1065 K – **PLAN: C2**
Ⓜ Kongens Nytorv
TEL. 33 11 15 37 – **www**.slotskaelderen.dk
Closed July, Sunday, Monday and bank holidays
Carte 205/340 DKK (lunch only) (booking essential)

Set in a 1797 building and family-run since 1910, this established restaurant sets the benchmark for this type of cuisine. The rustic inner is filled with portraits and city scenes. Go to the counter to see the full selection of smørrebrød.

TRIO ⅋⚬

MODERN CUISINE • DESIGN • FASHIONABLE ✗✗ ⪕ ⪑ A/C ⌷

Axel Towers (9th Floor), Jernbanegade 11 ⊠ 1608 V – PLAN: B3
Ⓜ København Hovedbane Gård
TEL. 44 22 74 74 – **www**.restauranttrio.dk
Closed Christmas, Easter, 1 January and Sunday

Menu 350/675 DKK – Carte 320/540 DKK

The highest restaurant in the city is located on floors 9 and 10 of the
striking Axel Towers building; enjoy a cocktail while taking in the view.
Accomplished dishes take their influences from both classic French
and modern Nordic cuisine.

UFORMEL ⅋⚬

MODERN CUISINE • FASHIONABLE • TRENDY ✗ A/C ⌷

Studiestraede 69 ⊠ 1554 K – PLAN: B3
Ⓜ København Hovedbane Gård
TEL. 70 99 9111 – **www**.uformel.dk
Closed Christmas-New Year

Menu 800 DKK – Carte 440/660 DKK (dinner only)
(booking essential)

The informal sister of Formel B, with gold table-tops, black cutlery, a
smart open kitchen and a cocktail bar (a lively spot at the weekend!)
Dishes are tasting plates and all are the same price; 4-6 is about the
right amount.

VÄKST ⅋○

MODERN CUISINE • RUSTIC • TRENDY   ⚔ ♿ 🏠 AC

Sankt Peders Stræde 34 ⊠ 1453 K – PLAN: B2
Ⓜ Nørreport
TEL. 38 41 27 27 – **www**.hostvakst.dk/vakst/restaurant/
Closed Sunday lunch
Menu 325/425 DKK

Dining outside 'inside' is the theme here, and you'll find plants,
garden furniture and a full-sized greenhouse at the centre of the
room. Interesting Danish cooking follows the seasons and is light,
stimulating and full of flavour.

D'ANGLETERRE

LUXURY • HISTORIC • CONTEMPORARY

🎋 ♿ 🖼 SPA 🎎 L♿ AC 🏊

Kongens Nytorv 34 ⊠ 1050 K – PLAN: C2
Ⓜ Kongens Nytorv
TEL. 33 12 00 95 – **www**.dangleterre.com

92 rm – ♦ 2750/4750 DKK ♦♦ 2750/4750 DKK, ⚏ 325 DKK
– 30 suites

MARCHAL ✿ – See restaurant listing

A smartly refurbished landmark hotel dating back over 250 years.
Well-equipped bedrooms come in various shapes and sizes; it's worth
paying the extra for a Royal Square view. Unwind in the basement spa
or the chic champagne bar.

COPENHAGEN MARRIOTT

LUXURY • BUSINESS • MODERN

≼ ⚕ ♿ ⟫ ⅃♨ AC ⚓ P

Kalvebod Brygge 5 ⊠ 1560 V – PLAN: C3
TEL. 88 33 99 00 – **www**.copenhagenmarriott.dk
402 rm – ♦ 1900/5000 DKK ♦♦ 1900/5000 DKK, ☕ 230 DKK
– 9 suites

A striking waterfront hotel; take in the views from the terrace or from the lounge-bar's floor to ceiling windows. Bright, spacious bedrooms are handsomely appointed and afford canal or city views. The popular American grill restaurant offers steaks, chops and seafood, and has a lively open kitchen.

SKT. PETRI

BUSINESS • BOUTIQUE HOTEL • MODERN

⚕ ⟫ ⅃♨ AC

Krystalgade 22 ⊠ 1172 K – PLAN: B2
Ⓜ Nørreport
TEL. 33 45 91 00 – **www**.sktpetri.com
288 rm – ♦ 1200/2000 DKK ♦♦ 1200/2000 DKK, ☕ 195 DKK
– 9 suites

Much of this 7-storey building is listed but it's been stylishly fitted out and displays modern Danish art. The basement restaurant P Eatery serves international cuisine and there's a nice garden courtyard with a wood-burning stove. Bedrooms are state-of-the-art and some have views over the city spires.

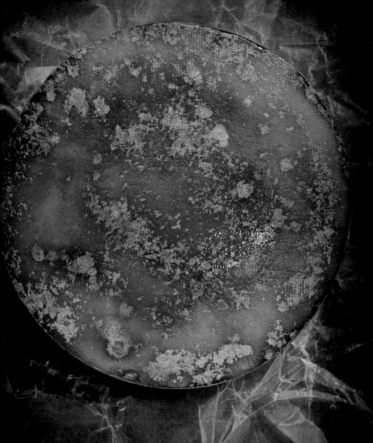

Arla Unika takes dairy to new heights. More flavour. More passion. More daring. Our cheeses and other dairy products are made by a passionate team of culinary experts who strive for excellence day in and day out. Constantly raising the bar is what Unika is all about. Visit arlaunika.dk to find out more.

ARLA
UNIKA
NYE HØJDER

NIMB 🏠

LUXURY • DESIGN • ROMANTIC

⛱ 🛏 🅰🅲 ⚒

Bernstorffsgade 5 ✉ 1577 V – **PLAN: B3**
Ⓜ København Hovedbane Gård
TEL. 88 70 00 00 – **www**.nimb.dk
38 rm – 🧍 2800/3000 DKK 🧍🧍 3900/5400 DKK, 🍽 255 DKK
– 12 suites
GEMYSE – See restaurant listing

An ornate, Moorish-style building dating from 1909, situated in Tivoli Gardens. Smart bedrooms are sympathetically designed and well-equipped – most overlook the gardens. Eat in the lively bar and grill, the formal brasserie or vegetable-orientated Gemyse. The rustic wine bar offers over 2,000 bottles – and you can enjoy Danish open sandwiches and snaps in Fru Nimb.

ADMIRAL 🏠

BUSINESS • HISTORIC • MODERN

⛵ ⛱ 🎋 ⚒ 🅿

Toldbodgade 24-28 ✉ 1253 K – **PLAN: D2**
Ⓜ Kongens Nytorv
TEL. 33 74 14 14 – **www**.admiralhotel.dk
366 rm – 🧍 1335/1825 DKK 🧍🧍 2275/2925 DKK, 🍽 150 DKK
SALT – See restaurant listing

An impressive 1787 former grain-drying warehouse, with an appealing maritime theme running throughout. Bedrooms feature vintage beams and bespoke wood furniture and have city or harbour views; opt for one of the duplex suites.

IMPERIAL

BUSINESS • TRADITIONAL • MODERN

☆ ৬ AC ᕊ 🚗

Vester Farimagsgade 9 ✉ 1606 V – **PLAN: B3**
Ⓜ København Hovedbane Gård
TEL. 33 12 80 00 – **www**.imperialhotel.dk

304 rm – 🚹 1300/2300 DKK 🚺 1600/2800 DKK, ☕ 185 DKK
– 1 suite

A well-known hotel, geared up for conferences and centrally located on a wide city thoroughfare. Bedrooms are particularly spacious and have a subtle Danish style. The contemporary restaurant features a brightly coloured Italian theme wall and serves Italian dishes to match.

ISLAND

BUSINESS • CHAIN • MODERN

⇐ ☆ 🏊 ৬ AC ᕊ P

Kalvebod Brygge 53 (via Kalvebod Brygge) ✉ 1560 V
TEL. 33 38 96 00 – **www**.copenhagenisland.dk

326 rm – 🚹 895/3450 DKK 🚺 995/5650 DKK, ☕ 185 DKK

Contemporary glass and steel hotel set just outside the city, on a man-made island in the harbour. Bedrooms are well-equipped – some are allergy friendly and some have balconies; choose a water view over a city view. The stylish multi-level lounge-bar and restaurant serves a wide-ranging international menu.

KONG ARTHUR

TOWNHOUSE • TRADITIONAL • CLASSIC

Nørre Søgade 11 ✉ 1370 K – **PLAN: B2**
Ⓜ Nørreport
TEL. 33 11 12 12 – **www**.arthurhotels.dk
155 rm - 🛇 800/1895 DKK 🛇🛇 1100/2300 DKK, ☕ 175 DKK

Four 1882 buildings set around a courtyard, in an elegant residential avenue close to Peblinge Lake. Well-equipped bedrooms have a high level of facilities. Relax in the smart Thai spa and enjoy complimentary drinks from 5-6pm.

NOBIS

HISTORIC BUILDING • LUXURY • DESIGN

Neils Brocks Gade 1 ✉ 1574 V – **PLAN: C3**
Ⓜ København Hovedbane Gård
TEL. 78 74 14 00 – **www**.nobishotel.dk
77 rm ☕ - 🛇 2500/3500 DKK 🛇🛇 2800/3800 DKK – 1 suite
NIELS – See restaurant listing

The impressive former music academy building sits close to Tivoli Gardens. Other than an impressive staircase, little of its 20C history remains; instead it's a cool, stylish and understated space with modern Danish furnishings.

RADISSON BLU ROYAL

BUSINESS • DESIGN •

≤ 🛎 👍 🏨 🛏 AC 🏊 🚗

Hammerichsgade 1 ✉ 1611 V – PLAN: B3
🅜 København Hovedbane Gård
TEL. 33 42 60 00 – **www**.radissonblu.com/royalhotel-copenhagen
261 rm – 👤 1195/6995 DKK 👥 1495/7495 DKK, 🍽 195 DKK – 2 suites

A spacious hotel designed by Arne Jacobson, with extensive conference and fitness facilities. Bedrooms have a Scandic style – the largest are the double-aspect corner rooms; Number 606 still has its original furnishings. All-day Café Royal has a designer feel and offers afternoon tea and weekend brunches.

SANDERS

TOWNHOUSE • ELEGANT • DESIGN

🛎 👍 AC

Tordenskjoldsgade 15 ✉ 1055 K – PLAN: D2
🅜 Kongens Nytorv
TEL. 46 40 00 40 – **www**.hotelsanders.com
54 rm 🍽 – 👤 2400/2600 DKK 👥 3100/6600 DKK – 6 suites

Set in a residential area close to Nyhavn and the theatre is this neoclassical Jugendstil-style townhouse. It is intimate, homely and elegant, from the cosy open-fired living room, atmospheric cocktail bar and small all-day brasserie to the sophisticated bedrooms where no detail is overlooked. A charming young team provide friendly, attentive and personalised service.

ABSALON

FAMILY • DESIGN • GRAND LUXURY

Helgolandsgade 15 ⊠ 1653 V – **PLAN: B3**
Ⓜ København Hovedbane Gård
TEL. 33 31 43 44 – **www**.absalon-hotel.dk
161 rm ⌑ – 👤 1100/2250 DKK 👥 1200/2350 DKK – 2 suites

A family-run hotel located close to the railway station and furnished
with vibrantly coloured fabrics. Elegant, comfortable bedrooms
feature an 'artbox' on the wall which celebrates an aspect of Danish
design such as Lego or porcelain.

ALEXANDRA

BOUTIQUE HOTEL • BUSINESS • DESIGN

H.C. Andersens Boulevard 8 ⊠ 1553 V – **PLAN: B3**
Ⓜ København Hovedbane Gård
TEL. 33 74 44 44 – **www**.hotelalexandra.dk
Closed Christmas
61 rm – 👤 695/1875 DKK 👥 795/2075 DKK, ⌑ 142 DKK

A well-run, late Victorian hotel in the city centre, with a contrastingly
modern interior. Bedrooms are individually styled and there's an
entire 'allergy friendly' floor; the 12 'Design' rooms are styled by
famous Danish designers.

ANDERSEN

FAMILY • DESIGN • CONTEMPORARY

Helgolandsgade 12 ✉ 1653 V – PLAN: B3
Ⓜ København Hovedbane Gård
TEL. 33 31 46 10 – **www**.andersen-hotel.dk
Closed 22-25 December
69 rm ⌂ – 🛉 1245/2195 DKK 🛉🛉 1445/2795 DKK

Bright, funky styling marks out this boutique hotel, where the bedrooms are classified as 'Cool', 'Brilliant', 'Wonderful' and 'Amazing'. There's an honesty bar in reception and you can enjoy a complimentary glass of wine from 5–6pm.

AVENUE

BUSINESS • FAMILY • MODERN

🏃 🅿

Åboulevard 29 ✉ 1960 C – PLAN: A2
Ⓜ Forum
TEL. 35 37 31 11 – **www**.brochner-hotels.dk
68 rm – 🛉 795/4000 DKK 🛉🛉 795/4000 DKK, ⌂ 160 DKK

A well-maintained, family-run hotel dating back to 1899. Relax around the central bar in the smart modern lounge or out on the courtyard patio. Bedrooms have a bright, crisp style and feature striking Philippe Starck lights.

CITY

BUSINESS • TRADITIONAL • GRAND LUXURY

Peder Skrams Gade 24 ✉ 1054 K – PLAN: D2
Ⓜ Kongens Nytorv
TEL. 33 13 06 66 – **www**.hotelcity.dk
81 rm ☕ – 🛉 1045/2745 DKK 🛉🛉 1145/2845 DKK

A modern hotel in a quiet street between the city and the docks. Bedrooms boast monochrome Jan Persson jazz photos and Jacobsen armchairs. Designer furniture features throughout and there's an eye-catching water feature in the lobby.

SKT. ANNÆ

BUSINESS • TOWNHOUSE • COSY

Sankt Annæ Plads 18-20 ✉ 1250 K – PLAN: D2
Ⓜ Kongens Nytorv
TEL. 33 96 20 00 – **www**.hotelsanktannae.dk
154 rm – 🛉 1000/4000 DKK 🛉🛉 1500/4500 DKK, ☕ 175 DKK – 1 suite

Three Victorian townhouses not far from the bustling harbourside of Nyhavn. Ask for a 'Superior' bedroom for more space and quiet; Room 601 is the best – it's accessed via the roof terrace and has its own balcony overlooking the rooftops. Dine on modern small plates in the restaurant.

HEBRON

TRADITIONAL • FAMILY • FUNCTIONAL

Helgolandsgade 4 ⊠ 1653 V – PLAN: B3
Ⓜ København Hovedbane Gård
TEL. 33 31 69 06 – **www**.hebron.dk
Closed 22 December-2 January
99 rm ⌂ – ♦ 700/1900 DKK ♦♦ 900/2100 DKK – 2 suites

A smart hotel behind a Victorian façade – this was one of the city's biggest when it opened in 1899 and some original features still remain. There's a comfy lounge and a grand breakfast room; well-kept bedrooms range in shape and size.

IBSENS

HISTORIC • FAMILY • PERSONALISED

Ⓟ

Vendersgade 23 ⊠ 1363 K – PLAN: B2
Ⓜ Nørreport
TEL. 33 13 19 13 – **www**.arthurhotels.dk
118 rm ⌂ – ♦ 880/2445 DKK ♦♦ 1230/2820 DKK

The little sister to Kong Arthur is this simple, brightly furnished hotel with a relaxed, bohemian feel. The small bar serves breakfast, as well as complimentary drinks from 5-6pm. Bedrooms are well-kept – 'Tiny' really are compact.

PAUSTIAN 🍴

DANISH • FASHIONABLE • DESIGN   XX ⟨ 🏠 **P**

Kalkbrænderiløbskaj 2
(North: 4 km by Folke Bernadottes Allé) ✉ 2100 Ø
TEL. 39 18 55 01 – **www**.paustian.com
Closed July, 23 December-14 January and Sunday

Carte 420/435 DKK (lunch only) (booking advisable)

A friendly, informal restaurant set in an impressive harbourside building designed by renowned architect Jørn Utzon. Traditional Danish cooking has French touches; watch the chefs at work in the open kitchen.

JORDNÆR ✿

DANISH • ROMANTIC • INTIMATE   XX ⟷ **P**

Gentofte Hotel, Gentoftegade 29
(North : 8km by Ostbanegade and Road 2) ✉ 2820
TEL. 22 40 80 20 – **www**.restaurantjordnaer.dk
Closed 24-30 December, Sunday and Monday

Menu 500/750 DKK (dinner only) (tasting menu only) (booking essential)

Chef:
Eric Kragh Vildgaard

Specialities:
Scallops, white currants and aromatic herbs. Duck with beetroot and truffle. Blackberry, sheep's milk and verbena

The passionately run 'Down to earth' is housed within an unassuming suburban hotel. The building dates from 1666 and the rustic modern room comes with grey painted timbers. The daily menu offer 3, 5 or 7 courses; knowledgeably prepared dishes feature ingredients foraged by the chef and flavours are harmonious.

SØLLERØD KRO ✿

MODERN CUISINE • INN • ELEGANT

Søllerødvej 35 (North: 20 km by Nørre Allé) ✉ 2840
TEL. 45 80 25 05 – **www**.soelleroed-kro.dk
Closed 3 weeks July, 1 week February, Easter, Sunday dinner, Monday and Tuesday
Menu 395/1095 DKK – Carte 910/1410 DKK

Specialities:

Oscietra caviar 'en surprise'. Black lobster, vin jaune and creamed morels. Gourmandise desserts.

A characterful 17C thatched inn by a pond in a picturesque village, with a delightful courtyard terrace and three elegant, intimate rooms. In keeping with the surroundings, cooking has a classical heart but is presented in a modern style. Dishes have deceptive depth and the wine list is a tome of beauty.

Søllerød Kro • 101cats/iStock

AARHUS

Denmark

Known as the world's smallest big city, Denmark's second city is a vibrant, versatile place, yet has the charm of a small town. It was originally founded by the Vikings in the 8th century and has been an important trading centre ever since. It's set on the Eastern edge of Jutland and is the country's main port; lush forests surround it, and there are beautiful beaches to the north and south. It's easy to enjoy the great outdoors, while also benefiting from the advantages of urban life. There's plenty to see and do, and most of it is within walking distance: the city centre is awash with shops – from big chains to quirky boutiques – as well as museums, bars and restaurants,

and the student population contributes to its youthful feel. The most buzzing area is Aboulevarden; a pedestrianized street which runs alongside the river, lined with clubs and cafés. Cultural activities are also high on the agenda of the European Capital of Culture 2017: visit the 12th century Cathedral and the ARoS Art Museum with its colourful rooftop panorama; witness the 2000 year old Grauballe man on display at the Moesgaard prehistoric museum; or step back in time at Den Gamle By. This is not a place that stands still and bold redevelopment projects are reshaping the cityscape, with shiny new apartment and office blocks springing up around the harbour.

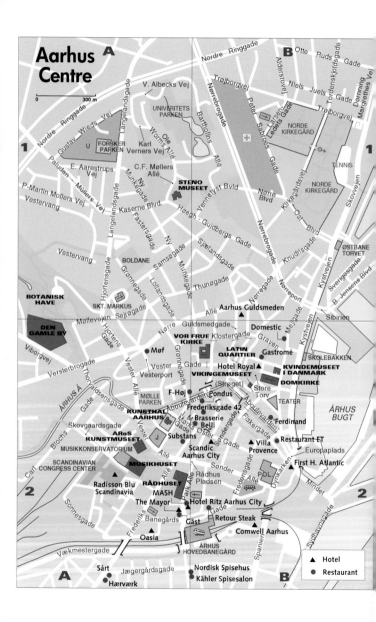

Aarhus A
Centre

B Otte Ruds Gade

0   300 m

Nordre Ringgade

V. Albecks Vej

Trøjborgvej

UNIVÄRITETS
PARKEN

Niels Juels Gade

Tordenskjoldsgade

Dronning Margrethes Vej

Gustav Wieds Vej

Langelandsgade

Ole Worms Allé

Nørrebrogade

Peter Sabroes Gade

Larsens Leders Gade

NORDE
KIRKEGÅRD

Trøjborgvej

FORSKER
PARKEN

Karl
Verners Vej

C.F. Møllers
Allé

Bartholins Allé

Nørre
Blvd

NORDE
KIRKEGÅRD

TENNIS

Skovvejen

E. Aarestrups
Vej

STENO
MUSEET

Kirkegårdsvej

Øst Blvd

ØSTBANE
TORVET

P-Martin Mollers Vej.
Vestervang

Paludan Müllers Vej

Ny Munkegade

Kaserne Blvd.

Høegh- Guldbergs Gade

Vennelyst Bvld

Nørrebrogade

Knudrisgade

Nørreport

Kystvejen

Sverigesgade

B. Jensens Blvd

Vestervang

Langelandsgade

Fastergsade

Ny Munkegade

Sjælandsgade

Samsøgade

Thunøgade

Nørregade

BOLDANE

Grønnegade

Lollandsgade

Nørregade

Kystvejen

BOTANISK
HAVE

SKT. MARKUS

Hjortensgade

Sejrøgade

Allé   Aarhus Guldsmeden

Sibirien

DEN
GAMLE BY

Møllevejen

Hortens Gade

Nørre   Guldsmedgade

Domestic

Viborgvej

VOR FRUE
KIRKE

Klostergade

Graven

Vesterbrogade

Thorvaldsensgade

Møf

Vester
Vesterport

Grønnegade Gade

LATIN
QUARTIER

Gastromé

SKOLEBAKKEN

ÅRHUS Å

Blochs

Vester Allé

MØLLE
PARKEN

F-Høj

Hotel Royal ▲

VIKINGEMUSEET

(Strøget)

Aboulevarden

Pondus

Frederiksgade 42

KVINDEMUSEET
I DANMARK

DOMKIRKE

Store
Torv

TEATER

ÅRHUS
BUGT

KUNSTHAL
AARHUS

AROS
KUNSTMUSEET

MUSIKKONSERVATORIUM

Skovgaardsgade

J

Substans

M M Brasserie
Belli

Mindegade

Øster Allé

Sønder Gade

Fiskergade

Ferdinand

Villa
Provence

Restaurant ET

SCANDINAVIAN
CONGRESS CENTER

MUSIKHUSET

Scandic
Aarhus City

Europaplads

First H. Atlantic

Radisson Blu
Scandinavia

RÅDHUSET

MASH

The Mayor

Rådhus
Pladsen

Park Allé

Frederiks Allé

Sønder

Sønnesgade

Carl

Banegårds

Hotel Ritz Aarhus City

Gåst

Gade

Dynkarken

Mindet

POL.

Spanier

Sydhavnsgade

Retour Steak

Comwell Aarhus

Oasia

Vækmestergade

Frederiks Allé

ÅRHUS
HOVEDBANEGÅRD

Sårt

Jægergårdsgade

Nordisk Spisehus

Kähler Spisesalon

Hærværk

▲ Hotel
● Restaurant

A

B

DOMESTIC ✿

MODERN CUISINE • FASHIONABLE • MINIMALIST   𝕏𝕏 ₺
🏠 🚗

Mejlgade 35B (through the arch) ✉ 8000 – **PLAN: B2**
TEL. 61 43 70 10 – **www**.restaurantdomestic.dk
Closed Christmas-New Year, Easter, Sunday and Monday
Menu 550/950 DKK (dinner only) (tasting menu only)
(booking essential)

Chef:
Morten Rastad and Christoffer Norton

Specialities:
Lobster with burnt cream and chanterelles. Pork with black garlic and onion. Buttermilk, herbs and fermented honey.

The hottest ticket in town is this elegant rustic restaurant where 4 friends work together to serve skilfully cooked, feel-good food with pure, natural flavours – using only Danish ingredients. Hanging hams, pickling jars and cookbooks feature. Menus offer 4 or 8 set courses; the fish dishes are a highlight.

FREDERIKSHØJ ✿

CREATIVE • ELEGANT • LUXURY   𝕏𝕏𝕏 ✿ ≤ 🚪 AC

Oddervej 19-21 (South: 3.5 km by Spanien and Strandvejen) ✉ 8000
TEL. 86 14 22 80 – **www**.frederikshoj.com
Closed 4 weeks midsummer, 1 week October, Christmas-New Year and Sunday-Tuesday
Menu 995 DKK (dinner only) (tasting menu only)
(booking essential)

Chef:
Wassim Hallal

Specialities:
Bresse chicken with peas and chanterelles. Danish lamb with textures of onions. Rhubarb with chocolate and caramel.

Set in the former staff lodge to the Royal Palace, this restaurant is smart, luxurious and contemporary with edgy artwork, iPad menus and floor to ceiling windows affording views over the gardens and out to sea. Dishes are elaborate, creative and visually impressive. Service is professional and knowledgeable.

Michelin • Jesper Rais/Restaurant Frederikshø

GASTROMÉ ❀

MODERN CUISINE • FASHIONABLE • INTIMATE   XX ⟷

Rosensgade 28 ✉ 8000 – PLAN: B2
TEL. 28 78 16 17 – **www**.gastrome.dk
Closed 25-26 December, Sunday and Monday

Menu 600/1000 DKK (dinner only) (tasting menu only)

Chef:
William Jørgensen

Specialities:
Halibut, Jerusalem artichoke and
watercress. Quail with chanterelles
and onions. Elderflower, white
chocolate and bee pollen.

This intimate Latin Quarter restaurant features a semi open plan
kitchen and stark white walls punctuated with contemporary art. The
menu is divided into a 'half throttle' of 4 courses and a 'full throttle'
of 8, with wines to match. Complex cooking showcases modern
techniques. Service is informative.

SUBSTANS ❀

MODERN CUISINE • FRIENDLY • SIMPLE   XX

Frederiksgade 74 ✉ 8000 – PLAN: A2
TEL. 86 23 04 01 – **www**.restaurantsubstans.dk
Closed Sunday-Tuesday

Carte 700/1000 DKK (dinner only) (tasting menu only)

Chef:
René Mammen

Specialities:
Brown crab, caviar and rose
hip. Organic pork with wild
onions, brown butter and herbs.
Raspberries with caramel, sour
cream and hazelnut.

Classically Scandic in style, with a fresh, uncluttered feel, Pondus'
older, more adventurous sister is run by the same experienced
husband and wife team. Creative, contemporary cooking uses top
quality, mostly organic, ingredients. Dishes have original touches,
distinct flavours and stimulating combinations.

Gastromé • Søren Gammelmark/Substans

HÆRVÆRK 😀

DANISH • INTIMATE • FASHIONABLE   🍴 ⑃ A/C

Frederiks Allé 105 ✉ 8000 – PLAN: A2
TEL. 50 51 26 51 – **www**.restaurant-haervaerk.dk
Closed Sunday-Tuesday

Menu 450 DKK (dinner only) (tasting menu only)

A lively place set in two converted shops and run by four enthusiastic friends. It has industrial-chic styling courtesy of a concrete floor, stark white décor and a glass-fronted fridge of hanging meats. Well-crafted Danish dishes have a rustic style and a refined touch. The daily set menu is great value.

PONDUS 😀

DANISH • BISTRO • RUSTIC   🍴

Åboulevarden 51 ✉ 8000 – PLAN: B2
TEL. 28 77 18 50 – **www**.restaurantpondus.dk
Closed 3 weeks July, 1 week Christmas and Sunday-Tuesday

Menu 295 DKK – Carte 315/355 DKK (dinner only)
(booking advisable)

Set by the narrow city centre canal, the little sister to Substans is a small, rustic bistro with a friendly vibe and a stripped-back style. The blackboard menu offers great value, flavoursome cooking which uses organic Danish produce. Dishes are bright and colourful and represent great value.

BRASSERIE BELLI ⅋○

CLASSIC FRENCH • BRASSERIE •
TRADITIONAL DÉCOR   ✗ 🏠

Frederiksgade 54 ✉ 8000 – PLAN: B2
TEL. 86 12 07 60 – **www**.belli.dk
Closed 1 week July, Easter, Christmas, Sunday and bank holidays
Menu 250 DKK – Carte 290/500 DKK

A long-standing, family-owned restaurant set on a pedestrianised city centre street. It offers good value, satisfying French brasserie classics and service is polite and friendly. Check out the owner's costumes from her circus days.

F-HØJ ⅋○

SMØRREBRØD • NEIGHBOURHOOD • FRIENDLY   ✗ 🏠

Grønnegade 2 ✉ 8000 – PLAN: A2
– **www**.fhoj.dk
Closed 4 weeks midsummer, 1 week October, Christmas-New Year, Sunday and Monday
Carte 275/395 DKK (lunch only) (bookings not accepted)

A bright, busy café with a pavement terrace; fridges and cabinets display a tempting selection of desserts, cakes, biscuits and drinks. There are six fresh, flavoursome classics on the smørrebrød menu; two plus dessert should suffice.

FERDINAND ⭐🍴

FRENCH • BRASSERIE • FASHIONABLE

Åboulevarden 28 ✉ 8000 – **PLAN: B2**
TEL. 87 32 14 44 – **www**.hotelferdinand.dk
Closed 23 December-4 January
Menu 445 DKK (dinner) – Carte 345/435 DKK

Red-canopied Ferdinand stands out from its neighbours on the liveliest street in the city. Classic brasserie dishes mix French and Danish influences; in the evening, choose a selection of small plates or go for the fixed price menu. A bar also serves tapas in the courtyard. Bedrooms are comfy and spacious.

FREDERIKSGADE 42 🍴

DANISH • NEIGHBOURHOOD • BISTRO

Frederiksgade 42 ✉ 8000 – **PLAN: B2**
TEL. 60 68 96 06 – **www**.frederiksgade42.dk
Closed 22-25 December, Sunday and Monday
Menu 220/530 DKK (dinner only) (tasting menu only)

The experienced owner extends a warm welcome to customers at this delightful restaurant in the heart of the city. The focus is on vegetarian dishes, with seasonal menus of well-priced small plates designed for sharing.

Ferdinand - Ferdinand • Lucas Adler Hyldebrandt/Frederiksgade 42 - Lucas Adler Hyldebrandt/Frederiksgade 42

GÄST ⅋⃝

ITALIAN • BISTRO • FASHIONABLE   ⋇ 🅿

The Mayor Hotel • Banegårdspladsen 14 ✉ 8000 – PLAN: A2
TEL. 87 32 0167 – **www**.restaurant-gaest.dk
Closed 23 December-8 January and Sunday

Menu 400 DKK – Carte 330/435 DKK

This spacious, relaxed Italian restaurant, set on the ground floor of
The Mayor Hotel, serves a seasonal, modern menu. Carefully cooked
dishes are full of flavour; everything is prepared in-house and the
pasta is the highlight.

KÄHLER SPISESALON ⅋⃝

SMØRREBRØD • NEIGHBOURHOOD •
TRADITIONAL DÉCOR   ⋇

M.P. Bruuns Gade 33 ✉ 8000 – PLAN: A/B2
TEL. 86 12 20 53 – **www**.spisesalon.dk
Closed 24-26 December and 1 January

Menu 200/410 DKK (bookings not accepted)

An informal smørrebrød café, popular with shoppers and open in the
evening. They offer soups, salads, smørrebrød and pastries, as well as
organic juices and top-notch teas and coffees. Monochrome pictures
of Aarhus add to the charm.

MASH ⅈ◯

MEATS AND GRILLS • FASHIONABLE • FRIENDLY

Banegaardspladsen 12 ✉ 8000 – PLAN: A2
TEL. 33 13 93 00 – **www**.mashsteak.dk
Closed 24-25 December and 1 January
Carte 365/700 DKK

This Modern American Steak House (MASH) is bright and smart, with colourful cow ornaments and red leather banquettes; sit in one of the booths. Top quality imported USDA steaks are listed alongside Danish and Japanese Kobe beef.

MEJERIET ⅈ◯

MODERN CUISINE • DESIGN • RUSTIC

Vilhelmsborg, Bedervej 101, Mårslet (South: 11 km by 451) ✉ 8320
TEL. 86 93 71 95 – **www**.restaurant-mejeriet.dk
Closed Monday-Wednesday and Sunday dinner
Menu 375/695 DKK (dinner only and Sunday lunch)
(tasting menu only) (booking essential)

Set within the old stables of a 19C manor in the heart of the countryside; the original brick floor and arched ceilings remain but it now has a clean-lined minimal look. The accomplished team offer beautifully presented, creative dishes.

MØF ⑩

DANISH • NEIGHBOURHOOD • TRENDY ✗

Vesterport 10 ⊠ 8000 – **PLAN: A2**
TEL. 61 73 33 33 – **www**.restaurantmoef.com
Closed 24 December, 1-2 January, Tuesday and Wednesday
Menu 325 DKK (dinner) – Carte 380/505 DKK (booking essential)

Ask for a seat at the counter to watch the young chef-owners cook
in the open kitchen. Lunch sees a selection of smørrebrød and
tarteletter, while dinner has a more modern style – dishes are Danish
at heart and made with local produce.

NORDISK SPISEHUS ⑩

MODERN CUISINE • NEIGHBOURHOOD •
FASHIONABLE ✗✗ AC

M.P.Bruuns Gade 31 ⊠ 8000 – **PLAN: A/B2**
TEL. 86 17 70 99 – **www**.nordiskspisehus.dk
Closed 24-26 December, 1 January and Sunday
Menu 270/850 DKK – Carte 500/850 DKK

An intimate restaurant with a unique concept: four themed menus
a year offering their own versions of dishes from Michelin Starred
restaurants around the globe. The décor changes along with the
theme: perhaps Japanese, Spanish or Nordic.

RESTAURANT ET ⅋○

FRENCH • DESIGN • FASHIONABLE ✕✕ ⅋ ⅋ ⅋ [AC] ⅋

Åboulevarden 7 ✉ 8000 – PLAN: B2
TEL. 86 13 88 00 – **www**.restaurant-et.dk
Closed Christmas and Sunday
Menu 360 DKK – Carte 375/515 DKK

You'll find charming service, modern brasserie styling and a central
kitchen at this well-run restaurant. Classic Gallic dishes are full of
flavour and some come with a Danish twist. There's also a superb
choice of French wines.

RETOUR STEAK ⅋○

MEATS AND GRILLS • FASHIONABLE • BISTRO ✕ ⅋

Banegårdspladsen 4 ✉ 8000 – PLAN: B2
TEL. 88 63 02 90 – **www**.retoursteakaarhus.dk
Closed 24-25 December and 1 January
Carte 240/595 DKK (dinner only)

A busy restaurant close to station: the latest outpost of the famed
steak group. They serve some simple starters and puddings but the
main focus is on meat, with tasty Danish rib-eye in various sizes
accompanied by fluffy homemade chips.

SÅRT 🍴

DANISH • TAPAS BAR • RUSTIC

Jægergårdsgade 6 ✉ 8000 – PLAN: A2
TEL. 86 12 00 70 – **www**.saart.dk
Closed 19-26 December, Sunday lunch and Monday
Menu 250/350 DKK – Carte 200/375 DKK

A simple but serious restaurant with its own deli: the first thing you see is a chiller filled with cured meats and preserved legs of ham; they also import whole cheeses, make their own pasta and have fresh bread delivered daily.

COMWELL AARHUS 🏨

BUSINESS • MODERN • DESIGN

Værkmestergade 2 ✉ 8000 – PLAN: B2
TEL. 86 72 80 00 – **www**.comwellaarhus.dk
240 rm ☲ – 🛉 1100/1900 DKK 🛉🛉 1300/2500 DKK

A stylish, modern hotel set over 12 floors of a tower block. With 19 meeting rooms, it's aimed at businesspeople; the largest has space for 475. Bedrooms are bright and contemporary with monsoon showers; choose a corner Business Class room for super city views. Guest areas include a bar and buzzy bistro.

RADISSON BLU SCANDINAVIA

BUSINESS • CHAIN • MODERN

Margrethepladsen 1 ⊠ 8000 – PLAN: A2
TEL. 86 12 86 65 – **www**.radissonblu.com/hotel-aarhus
234 rm – 𝝹 895/3245 DKK, 𝝹𝝹 995/3345 DKK, ☕ 175 DKK – 5 suites

A conference-orientated hotel close to the ARoS Museum. Spacious, contemporary bedrooms offer all the facilities a modern traveller would expect. Business Class rooms and suites on the top two floors offer the best views along with extra touches. International dishes are served in the informal restaurant.

SCANDIC AARHUS CITY

BUSINESS • CHAIN • MODERN

Østergade 10 ⊠ 8000 – PLAN: B2
TEL. 89 31 81 00 – **www**.scandichotels.com/aarhus
228 rm ☕ – 𝝹 700/2600 DKK 𝝹𝝹 800/2800 DKK – 8 suites

Behind the 19C façade of a Viennese Renaissance café lies a smart, modern hotel with an open-plan lobby, lounge and bar. Bright bedrooms feature photos of city scenes and the suites come with balconies. Solar panels supply electricity and rooftop hives provide honey. The Grill restaurant has an open kitchen.

VILLA PROVENCE

TOWNHOUSE • TRADITIONAL • PERSONALISED

Fredens Torv 10-12 ⊠ 8000 – PLAN: B2
TEL. 86 18 24 00 – **www**.villaprovence.dk
Closed 20 December-4 January
39 rm ☲ – ♦ 1295/1695 DKK ♦♦ 1395/3300 DKK

This charming townhouse is proudly run by an amiable couple and brings a little bit of Provence to Aarhus. Enter through the archway into a lovely cobbled garden designed by Tage Anderson, then head inside to be surrounded by books and French antiques. Bedrooms are individually styled; some have four-posters.

FIRST H. ATLANTIC

BUSINESS • CHAIN • MODERN

Europaplads 10 ⊠ 8000 – PLAN: B2
TEL. 86 13 11 11 – **www**.firsthotels.dk
102 rm ☲ – ♦ 995/1895 DKK ♦♦ 1095/2195 DKK

Although its exterior can hardly be deemed charming, its rooms are spacious and modern with good facilities, a balcony and a vista of either the city or the sea. Enjoy breakfast with a view on the top floor. Classic Italian dishes are served in the smart restaurant. Gym membership is available at the adjacent fitness club.

HOTEL RITZ AARHUS CITY

HISTORIC • TRADITIONAL • ART DÉCO

Banegårdspladsen 12 ⊠ 8000 – **PLAN: A2**

TEL. 86 13 44 44 – **www**.hotelritz.dk
Closed 24-25 December
67 rm ☕ – ♦ 1000/1150 DKK ♦♦ 1150/1350 DKK

An iconic 1932 hotel in distinctive yellow brick, situated opposite the railway station. It's friendly and welcoming with an appealing art deco style and neat, modern bedrooms in warm colours; most rooms have a shower only.

HOTEL ROYAL

HISTORIC • TRADITIONAL • CLASSIC

Store Torv 4 ⊠ 8000 – **PLAN: B2**
TEL. 86 12 00 11 – **www**.hotelroyal.dk
63 rm – ♦ 995/1895 DKK ♦♦ 1195/2095 DKK, ☕ 95 DKK – 5 suites

Beside the cathedral is the city's oldest hotel; 2018 marks its 180th birthday and it has a wonderfully classical feel – enhanced by paintings depicting Denmark's Kings and Queens. Very spacious bedrooms combine antique furniture and modern facilities. The informal restaurant serves international dishes.

THE MAYOR

FAMILY • TOWNHOUSE • MODERN

Banegårdspladsen 14 ⊠ 8000 – **PLAN: A2**
TEL. 87 32 01 00 – **www**.themayor.dk
162 rm 🖵 – 🛉 795/1995 DKK 🛉🛉 1045/2095 DKK
GÄST – See restaurant listing

Recently refurbished in a contemporary style, this hotel is situated close to the train station and has been owned by the same family for over twenty years. Cosy bedrooms have a modern industrial feel.

AARHUS GULDSMEDEN

TOWNHOUSE • TRADITIONAL • PERSONALISED

Guldsmedgade 40 ⊠ 8000 – **PLAN: B1**
TEL. 86 13 45 50 – **www**.guldsmedenhotels.com
22 rm 🖵 – 🛉 945/1345 DKK 🛉🛉 1075/1475 DKK

A relaxed hotel with an eco/organic ethos and a friendly atmosphere. Simply decorated bedrooms vary in shape and size; some feature antique furniture and the larger ones have four-posters. They offer complimentary tea, coffee and juice.

OASIS

TOWNHOUSE • TRADITIONAL • DESIGN

🅿

Kriegersvej 27-31 ✉ 8000 – **PLAN: A2**
TEL. 87 32 37 15 – **www**.hoteloasia.com
Closed 23-26 December
65 rm ☕ – 👤 900/1400 DKK 👫 1000/1650 DKK

After a day's sightseeing or shopping, you will be happy to head back to this hotel in a quieter area of the city. Bright, uncluttered bedrooms offer good facilities; go for one of the suites with their modern four-posters.

KADEAU BORNHOLM ❀

CREATIVE • MINIMALIST • SIMPLE

Baunevej 18, Vestre Sømark Pedersker, Åkirkeby (Southeast: 23 km by 38) ✉ 3720
TEL. 56 97 82 50 – **www**.kadeau.dk
Closed mid September-mid May

Menu 900/1200 DKK (dinner only and lunch July-August)
(tasting menu only) (booking essential)

Chef:
Nicolai Nørregaard
Specialities:
Scallop, horseradish cream with blue mussel paste. Pumpkin, wood ants and fig leaf oil. Berries, sour cream and gooseberry juice.

A remote beachside eatery with a superb sea panorama; this is best enjoyed from the terrace, although all tables have a view. The atmosphere is relaxed but they are serious about food here, with a 5 or 8 course tasting menu offering accomplished, original cooking with superbly balanced, contrasting flavours.

STAMMERSHALLE BADEHOTEL ❐

MODERN CUISINE • CONTEMPORARY DÉCOR

Sdr. Strandvej 128, Stammershalle, Gudhjem (Northeast: 24 km by 159 on 158) ✉ 3760
TEL. 56 48 42 10 – **www**.stammershalle-badehotel.dk
Closed 1 November-28 February, Sunday-Tuesday in October, March and April.

Menu 245/595 DKK – Carte 285/310 DKK (dinner only and lunch mid June-August) (booking essential)

A light and airy New England style restaurant in a charming coastal hotel, offering stunning sea views. Seasonal island ingredients are prepared with skill and passion by the young kitchen and the modern dishes have distinct flavours and interesting combinations. In summer they open at lunch for smørrebrød.

STAMMERSHALLE BADEHOTEL

LUXURY • SEASIDE

Sdr. Strandvej 128, Stammershalle, Gudhjem (Northeast: 24 km by
159 on 158) ✉ 3760
TEL. 56 48 42 10 – **www**.stammershalle-badehotel.dk
Closed 1 November-28 February

15 rm ⌂ – 🛉 950 DKK 🛉🛉 1150/1500 DKK

STAMMERSHALLE BADEHOTEL – See restaurant listing

This cosy hotel opened in 1911 and is run with passion. Stylish whilst
also respecting tradition, it is situated in an enviable position and
boasts superb sea views – you can even go bathing in the Baltic
just across the road. Bedrooms have straightforward comforts and a
simple Scandinavian style.

MOLSKROEN 🍴

MODERN CUISINE • CONTEMPORARY DÉCOR •
DESIGN

Molskroen Hotel • Hovedgaden 16, Femmøller Strand
(Northwest: 7 km by 21) ✉ 8400
TEL. 86 36 22 00 – **www**.molskroen.dk
Closed Christmas, January, Sunday-Wednesday February-22 March
and lunch September-mid March

Menu 650/1000 DKK – Carte 700/2200 DKK (booking essential)

A stylish, relaxed and well-regarded seaside inn with a reputation
for gastronomy; a table on the charming terrace is the perfect
spot to enjoy traditional French cuisine as well as more modern
interpretations of the classics.

MOLSKROEN

INN • LUXURY • CONTEMPORARY

← 🐴 ⛄ 🏄 🅿

Hovedgaden 16, Femmøller Strand (Northwest: 7 km by 21) ✉ 8400
TEL. 86 36 22 00 – **www**.molskroen.dk
Closed January and Sunday-Wednesday February-March

8 rm – 🛉 1280 DKK 🛉🛉 1680 DKK – 10 suites ☕ – 🛉 3500 DKK 🛉🛉
3500 DKK

MOLSKROEN – See restaurant listing

This inn, located in Mols Bjerge National Park, was built by renowned
architect Egil Fischer in 1923 and over the years it has gained a
considerable reputation. The traditional timbered façade contrasts
with its stylish, modern interior.

KOKS ❀

CREATIVE • CONTEMPORARY DÉCOR • INTIMATE   XX ←

Í Geilini 13, Kirkjubøur (11 km south of Tórshavn by 12) ✉ 175
TEL. 333 999 – **www**.koks.fo
Closed October-April and Sunday

Menu 1400 DKK (dinner only) (tasting menu only)
(booking essential)

Specialities:
Turf-smoked langoustine with
pine. Fulmar with beetroot. Dulse
seaweed dessert with blueberries.

Located in a remote coastal hamlet, with stunning views over the
fjords. The chef comes from the island – as do the excellent ingredients
– and the kitchen uses both modern and more traditional techniques
like drying, fermenting, smoking and salting to create accomplished,
imaginative, intensely flavoured dishes.

TI TRIN NED ❀

MODERN CUISINE • INTIMATE • HISTORIC   XxX

Norgesgade 3 ✉ 7000
TEL. 75 93 33 55 – **www**.titrinned.dk
Closed July, Christmas, Sunday-Tuesday
Menu 1500 DKK – Carte 695/755 DKK (dinner only)
(booking essential)

Chef:
Rainer Gassner
Specialities:
Turbot, braised cauliflower and
caramelised buttermilk. Duroc
pork with kale and summer truffle.
Strawberry terrine, rose hip and
crispy burnt cream.

Its name means 'ten steps down', which is exactly the number you'll take from the pretty rear courtyard to the vaulted cellar of this 19C building. It's run by an experienced couple and menus are guided by produce from their own garden. Cooking is original yet understated, well-balanced and full of flavour.

HENNE KIRKEBY KRO ❀❀

CLASSIC CUISINE • INN • FRIENDLY   XxX 🛁 🛏 ♿ **P**

Strandvejen 234 ✉ 6854
TEL. 75 25 54 00 – **www**.hennekirkebykro.dk
Closed 18 December-1 March, Wednesday dinner
March-April and Sunday-Wednesday lunch
Menu 595/1250 DKK (tasting menu only) (booking essential)

Chef:
Paul Cunningham
Specialities:
Danish lobster with chilled garden
minestrone. Varde Ådal lamb
with spinach, mint and garlic.
Strawberries, honey and lavender
ice cream.

A charming 18C thatched inn with a contrastingly modern interior. Top-notch seasonal produce celebrates their kitchen garden and the surrounding farmland. Cooking is founded on the classics and dishes are original and technically accomplished – the sauces are sublime. Service is attentive and very personable. Luxurious, super-stylish bedrooms complete the picture.

BRYGHUSET VENDIA - GOURMET

CREATIVE • INTIMATE • CONTEMPORARY DÉCOR

Markedsgade 9 ✉ 9800
TEL. 98 92 22 29 - **www**.bryghusetvendia.dk
Closed 2 weeks July, 29-31 December and Sunday-Wednesday
Menu 2000 DKK (dinner only) (surprise menu only) (booking essential)

A microbrewery with a stylish brasserie and a tiny gourmet restaurant. The latter consists of just three tables and serves an 11 course themed surprise menu of creative, elaborately presented dishes, designed to stimulate the taste buds.

SLOTSKØKKENET ✿

CREATIVE • INTIMATE • FRIENDLY

Dragsholm Slot Hotel • Dragsholm Allé (Northwest: 6.5 km by 231 on 225) ✉ 4534
TEL. 59 65 33 00 - **www**.dragsholm-slot.dk
Closed Sunday, Monday and restricted opening November-mid April
Menu 900/1100 DKK (dinner only) (tasting menu only) (booking essential)

Specialities:

Langoustine with red berries and herbs. Fried monkfish and salad with nasturtium. Strawberries with fermented water mint.

This atmospheric cellar restaurant is set in the former kitchens of an impressive 800 year old castle. Innovative, accomplished, intensely flavoured cooking has herbs and vegetables from the country's most fertile region at its core - many foraged by the head chef. A 5 or 7 course menu satisfies all the senses.

DRAGSHOLM SLOT

HISTORIC BUILDING • GRAND LUXURY •

Dragsholm Allé (Northwest: 6.5 km by 231 on 225) ✉ 4534
TEL. 59 65 33 00 – **www**.dragsholm-slot.dk
Closed 24 December

34 rm ☐ – ♦ 1995 DKK ♦♦ 2195/3000 DKK
SLOTSKØKKENET ❀ – See restaurant listing

A charming 800 year old fortified manor house with beautiful grounds and a moat; one of the oldest secular buildings in Denmark. The interior is modern yet full of character, with luxurious, classically decorated bedrooms featuring antique furniture and four-poster beds. Dine in the relaxed bistro, Spisehuset, or enjoy a gastronomic experience in Slotskøkkenet.

SLETTEN 🍴

MODERN CUISINE • FASHIONABLE •
BISTRO

Gl Strandvej 137 ✉ 3050
TEL. 49 19 13 21 – **www**.sletten.dk
Closed 24 December-9 January, Sunday and Monday
Menu 750 DKK (dinner) – Carte 400/700 DKK (booking essential)

A relaxed former inn in a charming coastal village; most people head to the room with the sea view, although the others with their bold foodie pictures are equally as pleasant. Well-presented modern small plates make up the menu – 2-3 per person is about right. The wine list provides plenty of interest.

FRU LARSEN ⁑○

MODERN CUISINE • RUSTIC • COSY   XX 🅿

Fru Larsen Hotel • Østergade 1, Laurbjerg (South: 6.5 km on 587) ✉ 8870
TEL. 86 46 83 88 – **www**.frularsen.dk
Closed 15 July-5 August, 16 December-7 January, Sunday and Monday

Menu 630 DKK (dinner) – Carte 400/560 DKK

A long-standing hotel restaurant with a wood-panelled ceiling and a fire burning in the hearth. Light dishes are served at lunch and there's a set 5 course dinner menu. Dishes are well-presented, carefully crafted and full of flavour.

FRU LARSEN 🏠

TRADITIONAL • COSY

⌂ 🛁 🅿

Østergade 1, Laurbjerg (South: 6.5 km on 587) ✉ 8870
TEL. 86 46 83 88 – **www**.frularsen.dk
Closed 16 December-7 January and 15 July-5 August

16 rm ☲ – ♦ 900 DKK ♦♦ 1150/1350 DKK
FRU LARSEN – See restaurant listing

A cosy inn on the main road through a small town. Half of the spacious bedrooms are decorated in a traditional, fire-lit 'romantic' style, while the others have a modern, minimalist feel and either a Parisian, Colonial or Antipodean theme.

FALSLED KRO ⁝◯

CLASSIC CUISINE • ELEGANT •
COUNTRY HOUSE

XᵪX 🛏 🅿

Falsled Kro Hotel • Assensvej 513 ✉ 5642
TEL. 62 68 11 11 – **www**.falsledkro.dk
Closed Christmas, Monday and dinner Sunday

Menu 1075/1795 DKK (tasting menu only)
(bookings essential for non-residents)

A formal hotel dining room with rustic beams, a vast feature fireplace, an open kitchen and an extension overlooking the garden. Set 4, 6 or 8 course menus offer accomplished, classically based dishes with bold flavours and modern touches. Ingredients are top-notch and service is detailed and professional.

FALSLED KRO

INN • HISTORIC • ELEGANT

🛏 ⚹ ♿ 🅿

Assensvej 513 ✉ 5642
TEL. 62 68 11 11 – **www**.falsledkro.dk
Closed Christmas

19 rm – 👤 2175 DKK 👫 2975/3695 DKK, 🍽 285 DKK – 9 suites
FALSLED KRO – See restaurant listing

In a small village off the beaten track is this professionally run, historic inn with a hugely characterful interior boasting flagged floors, wooden beams and a pretty central courtyard. Some bedrooms are in the original building; others are in the charming period cottages across the road in the lovely gardens.

PASFALL ⅋⚬

MODERN CUISINE • FASHIONABLE • DESIGN ⅋⅋ A/C

Brandts Passage 31 ⊠ 5000
TEL. 23 27 00 00 – **www**.thomaspasfall.dk
Closed 15 July-1 August, 23 December-8 January, Sunday and
Monday

Menu 395/579 DKK – Carte 625/885 DKK

Watch the eponymous chef at work in the open kitchen of this bright,
contemporary restaurant. Top seasonal ingredients are used to create
robustly flavoured dishes which are classic in their foundation but
modern in delivery.

FREDERIKSMINDE ❀

CREATIVE • ELEGANT • INTIMATE ⅋⅋ ⟨ 🛋 🏠 P

Hotel Frederiksminde • Klosternakken 9 ⊠ 4720
TEL. 55 90 90 30 – **www**.frederiksminde.com
Closed 23-26 December, 1-10 January, Sunday-Monday and lunch
Tuesday-Thursday September-May

Menu 450/1195 DKK (tasting menu only) (booking essential)

Chef:
Jonas Mikkelsen
Specialities:
Salted halibut with leeks and
mussel juice. Dry-aged beef,
wild mushrooms and fermented
celeriac. Rose hip sorbet with
salted honey.

A spacious and airy hotel summer room with only 8 tables and an
aspect that takes in the garden and the fjord. Creative modern
cooking uses superb seasonal ingredients in original yet well-judged
combinations. Dishes are precisely crafted and attractively presented
and service is knowledgeable and professional.

FREDERIKSMINDE

COUNTRY HOUSE • ELEGANT • CLASSIC

Klosternakken 8 ✉ 4720
TEL. 55 90 90 30 – **www**.frederiksminde.com
Closed 23-26 December and 1-10 January

19 rm ☺ – ♦ 1145 DKK ♦♦ 1545 DKK

FREDERIKSMINDE ❀ – See restaurant listing

An attractive 19C house named after a former king of Denmark; it has a classic, understated style and offers superb views. Bedrooms are tastefully furnished, well-kept and comfortable; antiques and fine portraits feature.

RUTHS GOURMET RESTAURANT ⊪○

CREATIVE • FASHIONABLE

Ruths Hotel • Hans Ruth Vej 1 ✉ 9990
TEL. 98 44 11 24 – **www**.ruths-hotel.dk
Closed 2 weeks January, Sunday-Thursday except Tuesday-Wednesday July-August and Thursday May-June and September

Menu 595 DKK (dinner only) (tasting menu only)
(booking essential)

Your meal starts with a personal introduction from the chef at this seaside hotel in Denmark's most northerly town. Set 3, 4, 5 or 8 course menus offer creative, elaborate modern cooking. Opening times change throughout the year.

RUTHS

FAMILY • CONTEMPORARY •

⌂ ▣ ⋔ ⚒ 🚗

Hans Ruth Vej 1 ✉ 9990
TEL. 98 44 11 24 – **www**.ruths-hotel.dk
Closed 2 weeks January

52 rm ☞ – ♦ 2100/2400 DKK ♦♦ 2100/2400 DKK – 5 suites
RUTHS GOURMET RESTAURANT – See restaurant listing

A long-standing seaside hotel, where families are made to feel
particularly welcome. Bedrooms are spread over a number of
adjoining properties and are bright, comfortable and up-to-date.
Enjoy creative, modern cooking in Ruths Gourmet Restaurant or bistro
classics in the relaxed French Brasserie.

THE RESTAURANT BY KROUN ⁑◯

MODERN CUISINE • DESIGN •
INTIMATE   XxX ← 🛏 ᬓ 🄰🄲 ⇧ 🅿

Kurhotel Skodsborg • Skodsborg Strandvej 139 ✉ 2942
TEL. 27 90 28 64 – **www**.skodsborg.dk
Closed Christmas, Easter, July and Sunday-Wednesday

Menu 700/900 DKK (dinner only) (tasting menu only)
(booking essential)

A stylish, formal restaurant on the ground floor of a grand Victorian
spa hotel; each of the seven tables has a view across the water. Tasting
menus feature creative, elaborate, modern dishes. The chef's table
is popular.

Ruths - Ruths • Michelin - Michelin

SKAGEN

SKODSBORG

no

KURHOTEL SKODSBORG

LUXURY • SPA AND WELLNESS • CONTEMPORARY

no⟨ 🛏 ⚒ ⚐ 🖼 🚿 🛶 🏖 🏋 **P**

Skodsborg Strandvej 139 ✉ 2942
TEL. 45 58 58 00 – **www**.skodsborg.dk
83 rm ⌑ – 🛉 1400/2300 DKK 🛉🛉 1700/2600 DKK – 2 suites
THE RESTAURANT BY KROUN – See restaurant listing

nono

A grand hotel with a world-renowned spa; founded in 1898 and
recently rejuvenated by a substantial facelift. Luxury bedrooms have
a modern style; choose one with a balcony to make the most of the
view across the Øresund Strait. Enjoy a cocktail on the rooftop terrace
or a relaxed meal in the brasserie.

ME|MU ❀

MODERN CUISINE • INTIMATE • HISTORIC XX 🕸

Torvegade 9D ✉ 7100
TEL. 21 14 00 77 – **www**.memu-gourmet.dk
Closed Christmas, Easter, July and Sunday-Wednesday

Menu 650/950 DKK (dinner only) (tasting menu only)
(booking essential)

Chef:
Michael Munk

Specialities:
Lobster, sunchoke and mustard
seeds. Veal with black and white
garlic and trompettes. Rye bread
porridge, woodruff and whipped
cream

This brightly decorated cellar on a pedestrianised shopping street
provides a stylish backdrop for some sophisticated cooking. Well-
judged, intensely flavoured dishes respect Danish tradition but have
a subtle modernity; choose 12 or 17 courses. Ingredients are top-notch
and the wine list is outstanding.

nonononoSKODSBORG

VEJLE

Michelin • Michelin • Michelin

nononononononononononononononononononononononononononononononononononononononononononononononononononononononononononono

no

no

TREETOP ¶O

MODERN CUISINE • CLASSIC DÉCOR   XX ⩽ 🍴 🎹 A/C P

Munkebjergvej 125, På Munkebjerg Hotel
(East: 8.75 km by 24) ⊠ 7100
TEL. 76 42 85 00 – **www**.tree-top.dk
Closed July, Christmas-New Year and Sunday-Monday
Menu 525/895 DKK (dinner only) (tasting menu only)
(booking essential)

A smart, light-filled hotel restaurant with an impressive view over the treetops and Vejle Fjord. Enjoy an aperitif in the cellars while you choose 3, 5 or 7 courses (or the surprise 10 course menu); dishes are elaborate and original.

Ch. Boisvieux/hemis.fr

FINLAND

DISTINCTIONS

HELSINKI

Finland

Cool, clean and chic, the 'Daughter of the Baltic' sits prettily on a peninsula, jutting out between the landmasses of its historical overlords, Sweden and Russia. Surrounded on three sides by water, Helsinki is a busy port, but that only tells a small part of the story: forests grow in abundance around here and trees reach down to the lapping shores. This is a striking city to look at: it was rebuilt in the 19C after a fire, and many of the buildings have a handsome neoclassical or art nouveau façade. Shoppers can browse the picturesque

outdoor food and tourist markets stretching along the main harbour, where island-hopping ferries ply their trade. In a country with over 200,000 lakes it would be pretty hard to escape a green sensibility, and the Finnish capital has made sure that concrete and stone have never taken priority over its distinctive features of trees, water and open space. There are bridges at every turn connecting the city's varied array of small islands, and a ten kilometre strip of parkland acts as a spine running vertically up from the centre. Renowned as a city of cool, it's somewhere that also revels in a hot nightlife and even hotter saunas – this is where they were invented. And if your blast of dry heat has left you wanting a refreshing dip, there's always a freezing lake close at hand.

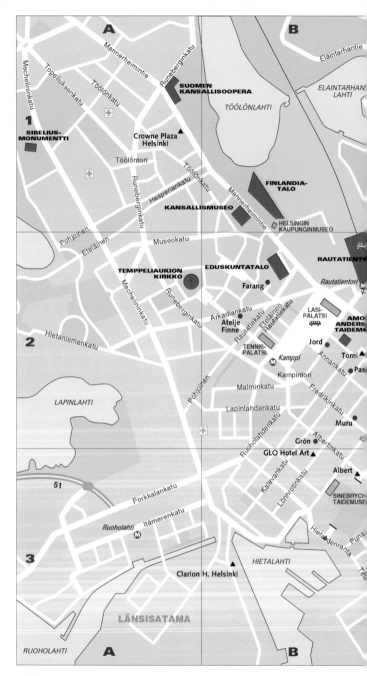

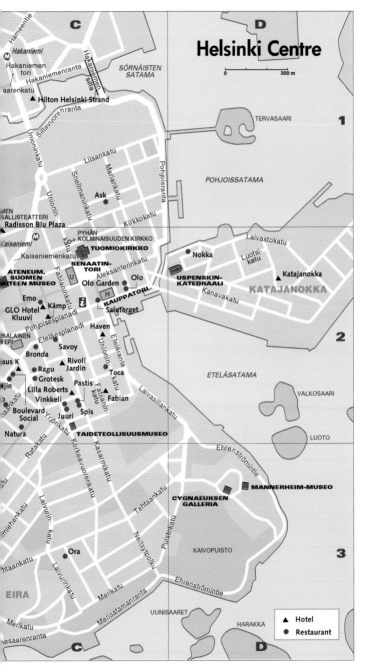

Helsinki Centre

0   300 m

C

Hämeentie
Hakaniemi
Hakaniemen tori
Hakaniemenranta
aarenkatu
Hakaniemen silta
Silitavuorenranta

▲ Hilton Helsinki Strand

SÖRNÄISTEN SATAMA

D

TERVASAARI **1**

POHJOISSATAMA

Unioninkatu
Liisankatu
Mariankatu
Snellmaninkatu
Ask ●
Unionin-
Kirkkokatu
Pohjoisranta

MEN ALLISTEATTERI
Radisson Blu Plaza ▲
Kaisaniemi
PYHÄN KOLMINAISUUDEN KIRKKO
Kaisaniemenkatu
TUOMIOKIRKKO
SENAATIN-TORI
Aleksanterinkatu
Nokka ●
Laivastokatu
Luotsi-katu
Katajanokka ▲

ATENEUM, SUOMEN TEEN MUSEO
Fabianinkatu
Olo Garden ● Olo
USPENSKIN-KATEDRAALI
KATAJANOKKA
Emo ●
▲ Kämp
KAUPPATORI
Kanavakatu
GLO Hotel Kluuvi
Pohjoisesplanadi
Salutorget
SALAINEN ERI
Etelänesplanadi
Haven ▲
Savoy ●
Bronda ●
aus K ▲
● Ragu
▲ Rivoli Jardin
Unionin-
Etelärante
2
ETELÄSATAMA
VALKOSAARI
ijin
● Grotesk
Pastis
Toca
Lilla Roberts
Vinkkeli ▲
Fabianin-katu
Fabian
Laivasillankatu
LUOTO
aankatu
Boulevard Social
Juuri
Spis
Natura ●
Yrjönkatu
TAIDETEOLLISUUSMUSEO
Ehrenströmintie
Ratakatu
Korkeavuorenkatu
Kasarmikatu
CYGNAEUKSEN GALLERIA
MANNERHEIM-MUSEO
iemenkatu
Laivurin-
Laivurin- katu
Tehtaankatu
Puistokatu
Neitsytpolku
KAIVOPUISTO
3
htaankatu
Ora ●
Laivurinkatu
Merikatu
Ehrenströmintie
EIRA
Merikatu
Merisatamanranta
UUNISAARET
HARAKKA
▲ Hotel
● Restaurant
esaarenranta

C
D

97

ASK ✿

MODERN CUISINE • INTIMATE • COSY   XX AC

Vironkatu 8 ✉ 00170 – PLAN: C1
Ⓜ Kaisaniemi
TEL. 040 5818100 – **www**.restaurantask.com
Closed Easter, Christmas, Sunday-Tuesday and bank holidays

Menu 50/110€ (dinner only and lunch Friday-Saturday)
 (tasting menu only)

Chef:
Filip Langhoff
Specialities:
Smoked reindeer tartare and
hazelnut. Pike-perch with brown
butter and caviar. Pancakes, spruce
and caramel.

It may be hidden away but this welcoming restaurant is well-known.
It's a charming place, run by a delightful, experienced couple, who
offer modern Nordic cooking crafted almost entirely from organic
ingredients. Dishes are light and original, produce is top quality and
flavours are clearly defined.

DEMO ✿

MODERN CUISINE • INTIMATE   XX

Uudenmaankatu 9-11 ✉ 00120 – PLAN: C2
Ⓜ Rautatientori
TEL. 09 22890840 – **www**.restaurantdemo.fi
Closed 3 weeks in July-August, 2 weeks Christmas, Easter,
midsummer, Sunday and Monday

Menu 60/105€ (dinner only) (tasting menu only)
(booking essential)

Chef:
Tommi Tuominen
Specialities:
Black Angus carpaccio with
oyster emulsion. Duck breast with
chanterelle porridge. Caramelised
brioche, fermented strawberry and
crème brûlée ice cream.

An unassuming-looking restaurant decorated in neutral tones and
hung with huge cotton pendant lights. Classically based cooking
combines French and Finnish influences to produce robust, satisfying
dishes with a subtle modern edge. Choose 4-7 courses; the menu is
presented verbally and changes almost daily.

GRÖN ✿

FINNISH • NEIGHBOURHOOD • INTIMATE

Albertinkatu 36 ✉ 00180 – PLAN: B2
Ⓜ Kammpi
TEL. 050 3289181 – **www**.restaurantgron.com
Closed Sunday and Monday

Menu 49€ – Carte 47/53€ (dinner only) (booking essential)

Chef:
Toni Kostian

Specialities:
Aged beef, chickweed and smoked
bone marrow. New potatoes with
summer onions and herring butter.
Wild strawberries with fennel
leaves and milk.

A warmly run restaurant where the open kitchen is the focal point
and the chefs bring the dishes to the table to explain them. Cooking
has a satisfying earthiness and clever use is made of both fresh and
fermented ingredients, with vegetables given equal billing as meat
or fish. Natural wines are well-chosen.

OLO ✿

MODERN CUISINE • DESIGN •
CONTEMPORARY DÉCOR

Pohjoisesplanadi 5 ✉ 00170 – PLAN: C2
Ⓜ Kaisaneimi
TEL. 010 3206250 – **www**.olo-ravintola.fi
Closed Easter, midsummer, Christmas, Sunday and Monday

Menu 65/120€ (dinner only) (tasting menu only)
(booking essential)

Chef:
Jari Vesivalo

Specialities:
Pike-perch with horseradish
mousse. Reindeer, salt-baked
celeriac and mushrooms. Aerated
honey parfait with sea buckthorn.

An attractive harbourside townhouse plays host to this cool,
minimalist restaurant, whose four rooms have a delightfully
understated feel. Lunch is 4 courses, while dinner arrives in up to
18 servings. Local meats such as moose and elk feature in exciting,
innovative dishes which are packed with flavour.

ORA ✿

MODERN CUISINE • CHIC • COSY

Huvilakatu 28A ✉ 00150 – PLAN: C3
TEL. 040 0959440 – **www**.orarestaurant.fi
Closed 22 June-24 July, 10 days Christmas-New Year, 1 week March, Easter and Sunday-Tuesday

Menu 85€ (dinner only and lunch Friday and Saturday)
(tasting menu only) (booking essential)

Chef:
Sasu Laukkonen
Specialities:
Pumpkin and zucchini tart with sea buckthorn. Whitefish from Inari with nasturtium. Blueberries with Douglas fir.

This small, intimate restaurant is run by chef-owner Sasu Laukkonen. The cooking focuses on local ingredients and uses modern techniques to enhance classic Finnish flavours. Dishes are served and explained by the chefs themselves.

BOULEVARD SOCIAL 🅶

MEDITERRANEAN CUISINE • FASHIONABLE

Bulevardi 6 ✉ 00120 – PLAN: C2
Ⓜ Rautatientori
TEL. 010 3229387 – **www**.boulevardsocial.fi
Closed Christmas, midsummer, Saturday lunch and Sunday

Menu 30/65€ – Carte 35/50€

Owned by the same people as next door Gaijin, this lively, informal restaurant offers an accessible range of authentic North African, Turkish and Eastern Mediterranean dishes; try the set or tasting menus to experience a cross-section of them all. If they're fully booked, ask for a seat at the counter.

EMO 🐾

MODERN CUISINE • FASHIONABLE • INTIMATE 🍴 ⅃ AC ⇔

Kluuvikatu 2 ✉ 00100 – **PLAN: C2**
Ⓜ Rautatientori
TEL. 010 5050900 – **www**.emo-ravintola.fi
Closed Christmas, New Year, Easter, midsummer, Saturday lunch and Sunday
Menu 39/54€ – Carte 50/76€

A laid-back restaurant with an adjoining bar, run by a friendly team. The menu is easy-going too, offering around 10 regularly changing dishes that can be taken either as starters or main courses. Good quality ingredients feature in flavoursome, unfussy preparations which come with a contemporary touch.

FARANG 🐾

SOUTH EAST ASIAN • SIMPLE • INTIMATE 🍴 ⅃ AC ⇔

Ainonkatu 3 (inside the Kunsthalle) ✉ 00100 – **PLAN: B2**
Ⓜ Kamppi
TEL. 010 3229385 – **www**.farang.fi
Closed Christmas, midsummer, Easter, last 3 weeks July, Saturday lunch, Sunday and Monday
Menu 32/64€ – Carte 30/65€

 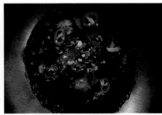

This stylish, modern restaurant is housed in the Kunsthalle art centre. One room is decorated with large photos of Thai scenes and has communal tables; the other is more intimate and furnished in red, black and grey. Zesty, harmonious dishes take their influences from Vietnam, Thailand and Malaysia.

GAIJIN 🏠

ASIAN • FASHIONABLE   🍴 ♿ 🛜 AC

Bulevardi 6 ✉ 00120 – PLAN: C2
Ⓜ Rautatientori
TEL. 010 3229386 – **www**.gaijin.fi
Closed Christmas, midsummer and lunch Saturday-Monday
Menu 39/64€ – Carte 39/74€ (booking essential)

Gaijin comes with dark, contemporary décor, a buzzing atmosphere, attentive service and an emphasis on sharing. Its experienced owners offer boldly flavoured, skilfully presented modern takes on Japanese, Korean and Northern Chinese recipes. The tasting menus are a great way to sample the different cuisines.

JORD 🏠

FINNISH • SIMPLE • FASHIONABLE   🍴 AC

Kortteli, Urho Kettosenkatu 1 (5th Floor) ✉ 00100 – PLAN: B2
Ⓜ Kamppi
TEL. 040 5828100 – **www**.restaurantjord.fi
Closed Christmas, Easter, Sunday and bank holidays
Menu 35/52€ – Carte 32/53€

The bright baby sister to Ask sits in a food court on the 5th floor of a shopping centre, surrounded by other eateries. Behind a large counter, the chefs prepare flavoursome, uncomplicated dishes using largely organic produce. The crockery and glassware are made locally and the service is warm and friendly.

ATELJÉ FINNE ⚏

MODERN CUISINE • BISTRO • FAMILY   ✗ 𝔸ℂ

Arkadiankatu 14 ✉ 00100 – **PLAN: B2**
Ⓜ Kamppi
TEL. 010 2818242 – **www**.ateljefinne.fi
Closed Christmas, Easter, midsummer, weekends in July, Sunday
and Monday
Menu 44€ – Carte 46/63€ (dinner only) (booking advisable)

This is the old studio of sculptor Gunnar Finne, who worked here
for over 30 years. Local art decorates the small bistro-style dining
rooms set over three levels. Regional dishes are given subtle modern
and international twists.

BRONDA ⚏

MODERN CUISINE • FASHIONABLE •
BRASSERIE   ✗ ♿ 𝔸ℂ ⟷

Eteläesplanadi 20 ✉ 00130 – **PLAN: C2**
Ⓜ Rautatientori
TEL. 010 3229383 – **www**.ravintolabronda.fi
Closed Christmas, midsummer and Sunday
Menu 29/57€ – Carte 36/70€

The floor to ceiling windows of this old furniture showroom flood it
with light. Have cocktails and snacks at the bar or comforting, boldly
flavoured, Mediterranean sharing plates in the brasserie. Each dish
arrives as it's ready.

GROTESK ⑪○

MEATS AND GRILLS • FASHIONABLE •
BRASSERIE   ✗✗ ⌂ AK̄ ⊙

Ludviginkatu 10 ✉ 00130 – PLAN: C2
Ⓜ Rautatientori
TEL. 010 4702100 – **www**.grotesk.fi
Closed Easter, 21-23 June, 24-26 December, 1 January, Sunday and
Monday
Menu 59€ – Carte 42/80€ (dinner only)

A smart, buzzy restaurant behind an impressive 19C façade.
It comprises a fashionable cocktail bar, a wine bar serving interesting
small plates, and a chic dining room which is decorated in black, white
and red and specialises in steaks.

JUURI ⑪○

TRADITIONAL CUISINE • BISTRO • INTIMATE   ✗

Korkeavuorenkatu 27 ✉ 00130 – PLAN: C2
TEL. 09 635732 – **www**.juuri.fi
Closed midsummer and 24-26 December
Carte 38/63€

A friendly bistro with colourful décor and a rustic feel. The focus here
is on sharing: small, tapas-style plates showcase organic produce and
classic Finish recipes are given a modern makeover. They brew their
own beer in the cellar.

Grotesk - Grotesk • H. Finer/Juuri - H. Finer/Juuri

MURU ⅋○

MODERN CUISINE • NEIGHBOURHOOD • TRENDY ⅋ ⅋ Ⓐ/Ⓒ

Fredrikinkatu 41 ✉ 00120 – **PLAN: B2**
Ⓜ Kamppi
TEL. 0300 472335 – **www**.murudining.fi
Closed Christmas, New Year, Easter, 1 May, midsummer, Sunday, Monday and bank holidays
Menu 46/52€ – Carte 46/52€ (dinner only) (booking essential)

The charming team really enhance your experience at this cosy little bistro. It's a quirky place, with a wine bottle chandelier, a bar made from old wine boxes and a high level wine cellar. A blackboard lists snacks and around 7 main dishes but most diners choose the 4 course daily menu with a Gallic base.

NATURA ⅋○

FINNISH • NEIGHBOURHOOD • DESIGN   ⅋

Iso Roobertinkatu 11 ✉ 00120 – **PLAN: C2**
TEL. 040 6891111 – **www**.restaurantnatura.com
Closed July, Christmas, midsummer, Monday and Tuesday
Menu 39/89€ – Carte 25/45€ (dinner only) (booking essential)

 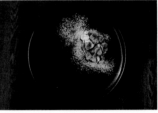

Carefully chosen ingredients are bound together in appealing seasonal small plates at this intimate restaurant. Techniques mix the old and the new and dishes are full of colour. Go for the 'Classic' menu, accompanied by a pure wine.

NOKKA ⁏○

MODERN CUISINE • ROMANTIC • RUSTIC

Kanavaranta 7F ✉ 00160 – **PLAN: D2**
TEL. 09 61285600 – **www**.ravintolanokka.fi
Closed Christmas-New Year, Easter, lunch July, Saturday lunch and
Sunday

Menu 47€ (weekday lunch)/58€ – Carte 50/72€

A huge anchor and propeller mark out this harbourside warehouse
and inside, three high-ceilinged rooms juxtapose brick with varnished
wood. A glass wall allows you to watch small farm ingredients being
prepared in a modern Finnish style.

OLO GARDEN ⁏○

MODERN CUISINE • SIMPLE

3206 250 • Pohjoisesplanadi 5 (Entrance on Helenankatu
2) ✉ 00170 – **PLAN: C2**
TEL. 010 3206250 – **www**.olo-ravintola.fi
Closed Christmas, July, Sunday and Monday

Menu 57/75€ – Carte 52/72€ (dinner only) (booking essential)

The casual addendum to Olo occupies a glass-roofed inner courtyard
and has a feeling of openness. The menu has a light, modern style and
some occasional Asian notes; some dishes are designed for sharing.
The cocktails are popular.

PASSIO ⅰO

MODERN CUISINE • FRIENDLY • NEIGHBOURHOOD   X   A/C

Kalevankatu 13 ✉ 00100 – PLAN: B2
Ⓜ Kamppi
TEL. 020 7352040 – **www**.passiodining.fi
Closed Christmas, midsummer and lunch Saturday-Sunday

Menu 29/50€ (booking advisable)

Exposed ducts, dimly lit lamps and leather-topped tables give Passio a faux industrial feel. Modern cooking showcases regional ingredients and flavours are well-defined. It's run by a local brewer, so be sure to try the artisan beers.

PASTIS ⅰO

CLASSIC FRENCH • BISTRO • NEIGHBOURHOOD   X   A/C

Pieni Roobertinkatu 2 ✉ 00130 – PLAN: C2
TEL. 0300 472336 – **www**.pastis.fi
Closed Easter, 4 November, 6 December, 22 December-
8 January, 22-24 June, Sunday and bank holidays

Menu 29€ – Carte 40/54€ (booking essential)

The clue is in the name: they serve classic French dishes, alongside several different brands of pastis. It's a popular place, so there's always a lively atmosphere. Come for Saturday brunch or have a private meal in Petit Pastis.

RAGU ⅈO

MODERN CUISINE • DESIGN • CHIC   XX ⅋ 🅰🅲 ⟐

Ludviginkatu 3-5 ✉ 00130 – **PLAN: C2**
Ⓜ Rautatientori
TEL. 09 596659 – **www**.ragu.fi
Closed July, Easter, midsummer, Christmas and Sunday
Menu 45/59€ – Carte 49/54€ (dinner only) (booking advisable)

Finland's famed seasonal ingredients are used in unfussy Italian recipes and the welcoming service and lively atmosphere also have something of an Italian feel. Choose the weekly 'House' menu to sample the latest produce to arrive.

SALUTORGET ⅈO

INTERNATIONAL • BRASSERIE • ELEGANT   XX ⅋ 🅰🅲

Pohjoisesplanadi 15 ✉ 00170 – **PLAN: C2**
Ⓜ Kaisaniemi
TEL. 09 61285950 – **www**.salutorget.fi
Closed Easter, Christmas, midsummer, Sunday and Bank holidays
Menu 35€ (weekday lunch)/45€ – Carte 30/60€

An old bank, located on the esplanade; now an elegant restaurant with impressive columns and attractive stained glass. The classic, brasserie-style menu has global influences. Enjoy afternoon tea in the plush cocktail bar.

SAVOY ⁉️🍴

MODERN CUISINE • ELEGANT

Eteläesplanadi 14 (8th floor) ✉ 00130 – **PLAN: C2**
Ⓜ Kaisaniemi
TEL. 09 61285300 – **www**.ravintolasavoy.fi
Closed Easter, Christmas, Saturday lunch and Sunday
Menu 65€ (lunch) – Carte 55/95€

The city's most famous restaurant opened in 1937 and offers impressive views from its 8th floor setting. Choose from updated versions of old favourites or a seasonal 4 course menu of refined, attractively presented modern dishes.

SPIS 🍴

MODERN CUISINE • NEIGHBOURHOOD • BISTRO

Kasarmikatu 26 ✉ 00130 – **PLAN: C2**
TEL. 045 3051211 – **www**.spis.fi
Closed Sunday, Monday and bank holidays
Menu 50/77€ (dinner only) (tasting menu only) (booking essential)

An intimate restaurant seating just 18; the décor is 'faux derelict', with exposed brick and plaster walls. Creative, flavoursome cooking features Nordic flavours in attractive, imaginative combinations. Most dishes are vegetable-based.

TOCA ⅋○

MODERN CUISINE • TRENDY

Unioninkatu 18 ✉ 00130 – PLAN: C2
TEL. 044 2379922 – **www**.toca.fi
Closed 22 June-31 July, 22 December-8 January, Sunday
and Monday
Menu 25€ (lunch)/65€ (booking essential)

A modest little bistro with an unfinished look. At lunch they serve just two dishes – aimed at local workers – while dinner offers a 3 or 5 set course menu. Cooking is an original mix of Italian simplicity and Finnish modernity.

VINKKELI ⅋○

CLASSIC CUISINE • ELEGANT • ROMANTIC   ⅋⅋ A/C

Pieni Roobertinkatu 8 ✉ 00130 – PLAN: C2
TEL. 029 1800222 – **www**.ravintolavinkkeli.fi
Closed 25 June-21 August, 22 December-9 January, Easter,
Saturday lunch, Sunday and Monday
Menu 29/54€ – Carte dinner 45/52€

A genuinely charming restaurant. The elegant, high-ceilinged room is smartly laid out and run by a delightful team, whose attentive and personable service will make you want to become a regular. The well-judged cooking is a pleasing mix of the modern and the traditional.

KÄMP

GRAND LUXURY • CLASSIC • HISTORIC

Pohjoisesplanadi 29 ✉ 00100 – PLAN: C2
Ⓜ Kaisaniemi
TEL. 09 576111 – **www**.hotelkamp.com
179 rm – 🛉 220/620€ 🛉🛉 220/620€, 🍽 32€ – 7 suites

The grand façade, columned interior and impressive staircase point back to this luxurious hotel's 19C roots and the classically furnished bedrooms follow suit; the superb spa, meanwhile, adds a modern touch. The chic bar serves an excellent selection of champagne and cocktails, while for dining, there's a bustling brasserie with an appealing globally inspired menu.

CROWNE PLAZA HELSINKI

BUSINESS • CHAIN • CONTEMPORARY

Mannerheimintie 50 ✉ 00260 – PLAN: A1
TEL. 09 25210000 – **www**.crowneplaza-helsinki.fi
349 rm 🍽 – 🛉 145/500€ 🛉🛉 145/500€ – 4 suites

A spacious hotel specialising in conferences. Comfy, up-to-date bedrooms have good facilities and city or lake views; the higher the floor, the better the grade. Pay a visit to the huge basement fitness club and spa, then make for the warm, welcoming restaurant which serves Mediterranean cuisine.

HILTON HELSINKI STRAND

BUSINESS • LUXURY • CLASSIC

John Stenbergin Ranta 4 ⊠ 00530 – PLAN: C1
🅜 Hakaniemi
TEL. 09 39351 – **www**.hilton.com
190 rm – 🛉 130/360€ 🛉🛉 165/395€, ⌂ 22€ – 7 suites

This spacious waterfront hotel has a classical 1980s design, an impressive atrium and an 8th floor fitness and relaxation centre; take in the view from the gym or pool. Smartly kept bedrooms boast marble bathrooms – ask for a room overlooking the water. The restaurant offers global classics and local specialities.

CLARION H.HELSINKI

CHAIN • BUSINESS • DESIGN

Tyynenmerenkatuz 2 ⊠ 00220 – PLAN: B3
🅜 Ruoholahti
TEL. 010 8503820 – **www**.nordichoicehotel.com
425 rm ⌂ – 🛉 100/150€ 🛉🛉 120/350€ – 16 suites

This smart skyscraper sits to the west of the city – take in the stunning view from the cool modern bedrooms or the 16th floor gym, outdoor swimming pool or Sky Bar. Meeting rooms are housed within a warehouse dating from 1937. The stylish ground floor bistro has a subtle American theme.

GLO HOTEL KLUUVI

LUXURY • MODERN • DESIGN

会 点 ⑨ 燃 ♨ AC 矤

Kluuvikatu 4 ⊠ 00100 – PLAN: C2
🅜 Kaisaniemi
TEL. 010 3444400 – **www**.glohotels.fi
184 rm ⌕ – 🛉 125/370€ 🛉🛉 230/380€ – 6 suites

A stylish hotel on a fashionable shopping street; a boutique sister to next door Kämp, whose spa it shares. Spacious bedrooms have a contemporary look and come with smart glass shower rooms. There's also a lively bar-lounge and a fashionable restaurant serving cuisine from around the globe.

HAVEN

BUSINESS • LUXURY • MODERN

会 点 ♨ AC 矤

Unioninkatu 17 ⊠ 00130 – PLAN: C2
TEL. 09 681930 – **www**.hotelhaven.fi
137 rm ⌕ – 🛉 160/300€ 🛉🛉 180/320€

A former city centre office block is home to this elegant hotel. Colourful modern bedrooms come with high ceilings, top quality furnishings and a plush feel. Extensive breakfasts are served in an impressive room. Snacks and light dishes are offered in the two cosy bars and they also have a great rum selection.

CENTRE

GLO Hotel Kluuvi - Markus Henttonen/GLO Hotel Kluuvi • Hotel Haven - Hotel Haven

FINLAND – HELSINKI 113

KLAUS K

LUXURY • DESIGN • PERSONALISED

Bulevardi 2/4 ⊠ 00120 – **PLAN: C2**
Ⓜ Rautatientori
TEL. 020 7704703 – **www**.klauskhotel.com
171 rm ⌓ – ♦ 120/320€ ♦♦ 140/640€

The Kalevala – a 19C work of poetry based on Finnish folklore – leads the design at this striking hotel, from the mosaic fish in the bar to the graffiti panelled corridors and stylish bedrooms. The Sky Loft rooms are particularly sumptuous.

LILLA ROBERTS

BUSINESS • DESIGN • PERSONALISED

Pieni Roobertinkatu 1-3 ⊠ 00130 – **PLAN: C2**
TEL. 09 6899880 – **www**.lillaroberts.fi
130 rm ⌓ – ♦ 150/210€ ♦♦ 170/220€ – 1 suite

This building was designed in 1908 by one of Finland's top architects and was originally head office for the city's energy works. The smart, designer interior uses dark colours and is centred around the concept of 'hygge' (enjoying the simple things in life). The elegant restaurant serves an appealing menu.

Klaus K • Klaus K • Michelin • Lilla Roberts

CENTRE

RADISSON BLU PLAZA

BUSINESS • CHAIN • CONTEMPORARY

🕏 ⓖ 🎿 ⅃⅌ 🅐🅒 🏂

Mikonkatu 23 ✉ 00100 – PLAN: C2
Ⓜ Kaisaniemi
TEL. 020 1234703 – **www**.radissonblu.com/plazahotel-helsinki
302 rm – 👤 120/389€ 👫 135/405€, ☕ 25€ – 1 suite

An elegant 20C building set close to the station and completed by
a more modern wing. Well-equipped bedrooms come in a choice
of modern or classic styles and many have 3D TVs. The bar is a
fashionable spot and the large restaurant – unusually set over several
rooms – offers five different types of cuisine.

TORNI

BUSINESS • ART DÉCO • ELEGANT

🕏 🅐🅒 🏂

Yrjönkatu 26 ✉ 00100 – PLAN: B2
Ⓜ Rautatientori
TEL. 020 1234604 – **www**.sokoshoteltorni.fi
152 rm ☕ – 👤 180/280€ 👫 180/280€ – 6 suites

A delightful early 20C hotel with a palpable sense of history.
Bedrooms come in 'Art Deco', 'Art Nouveau' and 'Functionalist' styles
– the latter, in the 11 storey tower, have glass-walled bathrooms. The
top floor bar has a terrace and superb city views; the restaurant offers
traditional Finnish cuisine.

FABIAN

TOWNHOUSE • CONTEMPORARY • MODERN

 ♿ ❎

Fabiankatu 7 ✉ 00130 – **PLAN: C2**
TEL. 09 61282000 – **www**.hotelfabian.fi
58 rm – ♂ 120/350€ ♂♂ 140/450€, ♻ 22€

A charming boutique hotel close to the harbour. Bedrooms have stylish black & white themes and smart bathrooms with heated floors. Have breakfast in the central courtyard in summer – ingredients are organic or from small producers.

GLO HOTEL ART

TOWNHOUSE • BUSINESS • MODERN

⚂ ♿ ❎ ❎ ❎ 🚗

Lönnrotinkatu 29 ✉ 00180 – **PLAN: B3**
Ⓜ Kamppi
TEL. 010 3444100 – **www**.glohotels.fi
171 rm ♻ – ♂ 150/300€ ♂♂ 165/365€

Sited in the heart of the lively Design District, a 1903 art nouveau castle with modern extensions and its own art collection. Chic bedrooms were styled by Finnish designers and come in three sizes. You can borrow everything from bicycles to paints and brushes. A Nordic grill menu is served in the old cellars.

KATAJANOKKA

HISTORIC • PERSONALISED • VINTAGE

Merikasarminkatu 1A ✉ 00160 – PLAN: D2
TEL. 09 686450 – **www**.hotelkatajanokka.fi
106 rm ☕ – 🚹 90/250€ 🚻 100/400€

A pleasantly restored, late 19C prison where they have retained the original staircases and high ceilinged corridors. The old cells are now comfortable, well-equipped bedrooms with modern bathrooms. The traditional cellar restaurant features a preserved prison cell and serves traditional Finnish cuisine.

ALBERT

BUSINESS • CONTEMPORARY • PERSONALISED

Albertinkatu 30 ✉ 00180 – PLAN: B3
TEL. 020 1234638 – **www**.sokoshotels.fi
Closed Christmas
95 rm ☕ – 🚹 129/185€ 🚻 144/200€

An unassuming 19C building with a contrastingly cosy interior. Good-sized contemporary bedrooms are well-equipped and come with Nordic furnishings and up-to-date bathrooms. Have drinks in the welcoming open-plan lounge-bar, then head to the trattoria-style restaurant for a selection of Italian classics.

RIVOLI JARDIN

TOWNHOUSE • COSY • PERSONALISED

 ᕕ 🜸

Kasarmikatu 40 ✉ 00130 – **PLAN: C2**
TEL. 09 681500 – **www**.rivoli.fi
Closed Christmas
55 rm ☲ – 🛉 100/240€ 🛉🛉 120/260€

A small, city centre oasis hidden away off a courtyard, with an intimate conservatory lounge, and a sauna and meeting room tucked away in the cellar. Bedrooms are cosy and individually decorated; the top floor rooms have terraces.

HILTON HELSINKI AIRPORT

BUSINESS • CHAIN • MODERN

☆ ᕕ 🜸 ⅃ᕒ ᴬᶜ ↫ 🛁 **P**

Lentäjänkuja 1 (North: 19 km by A 137) ✉ 01530
TEL. 09 73220 – **www**.hilton.com
330 rm – 🛉 99/370€ 🛉🛉 109/400€, ☲ 27€ – 5 suites

3mins from the international terminal (T2); a spacious glass hotel with a relaxed ambience and a large conference capacity. Well-soundproofed bedrooms boast locally designed furniture, good facilities and large bathrooms – some have saunas. The stylish restaurant serves Finnish and international cuisine.

KASKIS ⅋○

MODERN CUISINE • FRIENDLY • NEIGHBOURHOOD   ⅋ A/C

Kaskenkatu 6A ✉ 20700
TEL. 044 7230200 – **www**.kaskis.fi
Closed 3 weeks Christmas-January, 2 weeks midsummer, Sunday
and Monday
Menu 55/66€ (dinner only) (booking essential)

A very popular glass-fronted restaurant that always has a lively,
fun atmosphere. The kitchen uses good ingredients and dishes are
brought to the table by the chefs who explain their quite elaborate
construction in full.

katiisoup/iStock

ICELAND

DISTINCTIONS

REYKJAVIK

ICELAND

marchello74/iStock

Europe's youngest landmass is a country of extremes; a dramatic wilderness where volcanic springs sit beside vast glaciers and long summer days are offset by dark winters. Its largest city, Reykjavik, lays claim to being the world's most northern capital and its settlement by a Norseman over 1100 years ago is recounted in the Icelandic Sagas.

Two thirds of Icelanders live in Reykjavik, in low, colourful buildings designed to fend off the North Atlantic winds and brighten spirits through the long, dark nights. Other buildings

echo nature itself: the geometric shapes of the Hallgrímskirkja Church – whose soaring tower keeps watch over the city – mirror the lava flows, while the Harpa Concert Hall is cleverly designed to reflect both the city and nature – its cascading LEDs alluding to the incredible spectacle of the Aurora Borealis.

The historic city centre, known as 101, lies between the harbour and an inland lake, and is a bustling, bohemian place filled with independent boutiques and fashionable bars. Head out further east and you can discover the secrets of the Blue Lagoon's healing thermal waters and the Golden Circle, which comprises three of Iceland's greatest natural wonders: the Þingvellir National Park (where you can walk between two tectonic plates); the Haukadalur Geothermal Field with its geysers and mud pools; and the spectacular Gullfoss Waterfall – the largest in Europe.

Reykjavik Centre

0   200 m

FAXAFLÓI

PORT

HARPA

LISTASAFN
REYKJAVÍKUR

KOLAPORTID

Trygvagata

Hafnarstræti

ARNARHÓLL

STJÓRNARRÁDID

Austurstræti

AUSTURVÖLLUR

Geirsgata

Ingólfsstræti

Skúlagata

Faxagata

Sölvhólsgata

Sæbraut

101 ▲

Lækjargata

Laugavegur

Dill

▲ Borg

DÓMKIRKJAN

ÞING

ÞJÓDMENNINGARHÚSID

ÞJÓDLEIKHÚSID

SUN-CRAFT

Skúlagata

Sæbraut

A-HÚS

MENNTASKÓLINN

Canopy
by Hilton

Hverfisgata

Lindargata

Vatnsstígur

Laugavegur

THÉÂTRE
IDNÓ

Laufásvegur

Mímisstræti

Þingholtsstræti

Bergstaðastræti

Óðinsgata

Týsgata

Njálsgata

Skólavörðustígur

Lokastígur

Þórsgata

Grettisgata

Klapparstígur

Frakkastígur

NÝLISTASAFNID

Skúlagata

Sæbraut

Snorrabraut

Hverfisgata

SÆBRAUT

FRÍKIRKJAN

LISTASAFN
ÍSLANDS

Gallery

Hellusund

▲ Holt

Freyjugata

Baldursgata

Bragagata

Fjölugata

Laufásvegur

Soleyjargata

Njarðargata

Bergstaðastræti

LISTASAFN
EINARS JÓNSSONAR

LISTASAFN ASÍ

Mímisvegur

Alda

Vitastígur

Grettisgata

Barónsstígur

Njálsgata

Bergþórugata

Laugavegur

REDASAFN

Grettisgata

Njálsgata

HALLGRÍMSKIRKJA

Barónsstígur

Eiriksgata

Leifsgata

▲ Hotel

● Restaurant

C   D

1

2

3

DILL ❀

CENTRE

CREATIVE • RUSTIC • INTIMATE   ✗✗ ⇔ ⇔

Hverfisgötu 12 ✉ 101 – **PLAN: C2**
TEL. 5521522 – **www**.dillrestaurant.is
Closed 24-25 December, 1 January and Sunday-Tuesday

Menu 11900/13900 ISK (dinner only) (tasting menu only)
(booking essential)

Chef:
Ragnar Eiriksson

Specialities:
Smoked haddock with mashed
potatoes, skyr and sweet & sour
herb oil. Beef brisket, sunchokes
and angelica. Whey ice cream,
rhubarb and dried cake.

This small, dimly-lit restaurant has become a favourite destination
for New Nordic cooking. It resembles an old barn, and the best of
the island's produce is skilfully prepared at the central counter. Each
dish uses just a handful of ingredients but demonstrates complexity
in its textures and flavours.

MATUR OG DRYKKUR ☺

CENTRE

TRADITIONAL CUISINE • SIMPLE • TRENDY   ✗ ⅃ ⇔ 🅿

Grandagar_ur 2 ✉ 101 – **PLAN: B2**
TEL. 5718877 – **www**.maturogdrykkur.is
Closed 25 December and Sunday lunch

Menu 3590 ISK (lunch) – Carte 5070/8180 ISK

This simple little eatery is named after an Icelandic cookbook and
shares its premises with the Saga Museum. Old recipes are given
modern twists, resulting in delicious dishes with a creative edge. The
à la carte is supplemented by great value 'Icelandic Snacks', along
with various tasting menus at dinner.

GALLERY ⅃○

MODERN CUISINE • CLASSIC DÉCOR •
INTIMATE

XᵧX 🎕 ⼞ ⼢

Holt Hotel, Bergstadastraeti 37 ⊠ 101 – **PLAN: C3**
TEL. 552 5700 – **www**.holt.is
Closed Sunday and Monday
Menu 3900/14900 ISK – Carte 7650/13500 ISK (booking essential)

The island's oldest and most highly regarded restaurant sits within
the Holt hotel, and comes with red furniture and a huge art collection.
Classic French cooking uses top island produce; the cured salmon
recipe dates back to 1966!

GRILLIÐ ⅃○

MODERN CUISINE • CLASSIC DÉCOR •
ELEGANT

XX ⟨ AC ⼢ P

Radisson Blu Saga Hotel, Hagatorg ⊠ 107 – **PLAN: B3**
TEL. 525 9960 – **www**.grillid.is
Closed Sunday-Monday
Menu 10900 ISK – Carte 9250/12950 ISK (dinner only)
(booking essential)

Located at the top of a hotel; the unusual ceiling depicts the zodiac
signs but it's the 360° views that will steal your attention, especially
at sunset. The young team deliver an array of ambitious Nordic dishes
with clear flavours.

VOX 🍴○

MODERN CUISINE • CONTEMPORARY DÉCOR • ELEGANT ✗✗ ♿ A/C ⇼ ⇔ **P**

Hilton Reykjavik Nordica Hotel, Suðurlandsbraut 2 (East: 2.75 km by 41) ⊠ 108
TEL. 444 9050 – **www**.vox.is
Menu 3850/8900 ISK – Carte 6950/12870 ISK

A stylish restaurant and bar set off the lobby of the Hilton hotel. At lunch there's a popular hot and cold buffet; at dinner, choices include an à la carte and 'Season' and 'Seafood' tasting menus. Cooking is modern and creative.

101 ⌂

LUXURY • DESIGN • TRENDY
⇙ 🛁 🛖 🛗 A/C ⇼

Hverfisgata 8-10 ⊠ 101 – PLAN: C2
TEL. 580 0101 – **www**.101hotel.is
38 rm – 🛉 45900/59900 ISK 🛉🛉 54900/75900 ISK, ⊊ 2990 ISK

Behind the unassuming façade of the former Social Democratic Party offices, you'll find this sleek design hotel filled with interesting Icelandic art. Stylish monochrome bedrooms have stunning glass bathrooms; choose one with a balcony or a harbour view. The stylish restaurant with its long bar and glass ceiling is the perfect spot to try modern Icelandic cooking.

BORG

LUXURY • ART DÉCO • ELEGANT

Pósthússtræti 11 ⊠ 101 – **PLAN: C2**
TEL. 5511440 – **www**.keahotels.is
99 rm ⊑ – ♦ 28000/65000 ISK ♦♦ 35000/67500 ISK – 2 suites

Overlooking Austurvöllur Square is this carefully restored 1930s hotel which combines traditional elegance with modern comforts. Bedrooms encapsulate the art deco era with bespoke furnishings, wooden floors and elegant lines. The bar has a charming square counter and doubles as a restaurant.

CANOPY BY HILTON

BOUTIQUE HOTEL • CONTEMPORARY • TRENDY

Smidjustigur 4 ⊠ 101 – **PLAN: C2/3**
TEL. 528 7000 – **www**.canopybyhilton.com
112 rm ⊑ – ♦ 16100/32150 ISK ♦♦ 21500/42850 ISK – 8 suites

The first ever 'Canopy' sits just off the main street. It's a relaxed and stylish home-from-home; grab breakfast in the deli, borrow a bike or take in city views from the top floor terrace. Understated bedrooms feature natural materials, bespoke furniture and quirky artwork. Menus offer creative small plates.

HOLT

FAMILY • CLASSIC • COSY

Bergstadastraeti 37 ✉ 101 – PLAN: C3
TEL. 552 5700 – **www**.holt.is
42 rm ⌑ – 🛉 38000/48000 ISK 🛉🛉 38000/48000 ISK – 4 suites
GALLERY – See restaurant listing

The draws of this family-run hotel are its old world charm and quiet suburban location. The 4th floor bedrooms look out over the city, while the cosy lounge and cocktail bar are great places to appreciate their vast art collection.

ALDA

BOUTIQUE HOTEL • CONTEMPORARY • TRENDY

Laugavegi 66-68 ✉ 101 – PLAN: D3
TEL. 553 9366 – **www**.aldahotel.is
88 rm ⌑ – 🛉 21200/47000 ISK 🛉🛉 21200/47000 ISK – 2 suites

At the quieter eastern end of the main shopping street you'll find this fashionable hotel complete with its own barber's shop and a trendy bar offering simple meals. Bedrooms are simply but stylishly furnished with natural materials like Icelandic wool; the 4th floor rooms have balconies with sea views.

J. Arnold Images/hemis.fr

NORWAY

DISTINCTIONS

OSLO

Norway

Oslo has a lot going for it – and one slight downside: it's one of the world's most expensive cities. It also ranks high when it comes to its standard of living, however, and its position at the head of Oslofjord, surrounded by steep forested hills, is hard to match for drama and beauty. It's a charmingly compact place to stroll round, particularly in the summer, when the daylight hours practically abolish the night and, although it may lack the urban cool of some other Scandinavian cities, it boasts its fair share of trendy clubs and a raft of Michelin Stars. There's a real raft,

too: Thor Hyerdahl's famous Kon-Tiki – one of the star turns in a city that loves its museums. Oslo's uncluttered feel is enhanced by parks and wide streets and, in the winter, there are times when you feel you have the whole place to yourself. Drift into the city by boat and land at the smart harbour of Aker Brygge; to the west lies the charming Bygdøy peninsula, home to museums permeated with the smell of the sea. Northwest is Frogner, with its famous sculpture park, the place where locals hang out on long summer days. The centre of town, the commercial hub, is Karl Johans Gate, bounded at one end by the Royal Palace and at the other by the Cathedral, while further east lie two trendy multicultural areas, Grunerlokka and Grønland, the former also home to the Edvard Munch Museum.

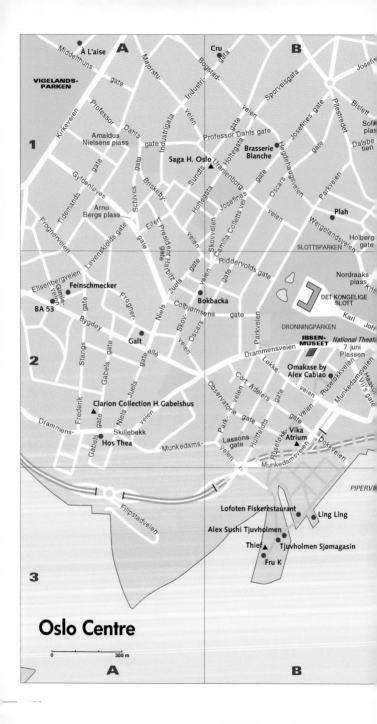

Oslo Centre

A L'aise

VIGELANDS-PARKEN

Middelthuns gate

Majorstu-

Cru

Bogstad-gata

Josefi

A

B

Sporveisgata

Pilestredet

Bislett

Kirkeveien

Professor Dahls gate

Industrigata

veien

Professor Dahls gate

Josefines gate

Sofi plas

Dalsbetien

1

Amaldus Nielsens plass

Saga H. Oslo ▲

Uranienborg

Brasserie Blanche

Heggeliveien

Oscars gate

Parkveien

Gyldenloves gate

Schives

Briskeby-

Holtegata

Sundts

Josefines

veien

Tidemands gate

Eilert

veien

Camilla Colletts vei

Plah

Frognerveien

Arno Bergs plass

Presidentt Harbitz

Juels gate

Skovveien

veien

Wergelandsveien

Holberg gate

Løvenskiolds gate

gate

Riddervolds gate

SLOTTSPARKEN

Elisenbergveien

Gimle-veien

Feinschmecker

Frogner-gate

Juels

Skov-

gate

Colbjørnsens

Bokbacka

gate

Parkveien

Nordraaks plass

Kris

BA 53

Stangs gate

Bygdoy

Gabels gate

Galt

Niels

alle

Oscars

veien

DET KONGELIGE SLOTT

DRONNINGPARKEN

IBSEN-MUSEET

National Theat

Karl Joh

2

Frederik

Gabels gate

Niels Juels gate

Drammensveien

Lekke-

Cort Adelers gate

Observatorie gate

Parkveien

Omakase by Alex Cabiao

7 juni Plassen

Munkedamsveien

Haakon VII's gate

Ruseløkkveien

Clarion Collection H. Gabelshus ▲

Skillebekk

Hos Thea

Munkedams-

Lassons gate

Hultfeldts gate

Ruseløkkveien

Vika Atrium ▲

Munkedamsveien

Dokkveien

Drammens-

PIPERV

Filipstadveien

Lofoten Fiskerestaurant

Alex Sushi Tjuvholmen

Thief ▲

Fru K

Ling Ling

Tjuvholmen Sjømagasin

3

0   300 m

A

B

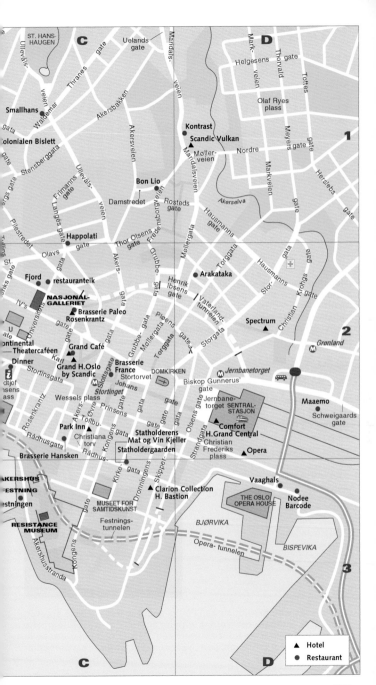

ST. HANS-HAUGEN

C

Uelands gate

Mandals-

D

Helgesens gate

Thorvald

Tottes gate

Ullevåls-veien

Thranes gate

Waldemar

Smallhans

gata

Olaf Ryes plass

1

Kolonialen Bislett

Stensberggata

Akersbakken

Akersveien

veien

Kontrast

Scandic Vulkan

Møller-veien

Nordre

Meyers gate

gate

Markveien

Herslebs

gate

Frimanns gate

Ullevåls-veien

Bon Lio

Fredensborgveien

Rosteds gate

Maridalsveien

Akerselva

Hausmanns gate

Langes gate

Pilestredet

Damstredet

Happolati

Thor Olsens gate

gate

Møllergata

Torggata

Hausmanns

Stor-

Krohgs gate

Olavs

Akers-

Grubbe-

gate

St.

Fjord

restauranteik

Arakataka

Henrik Ibsens gate

Vaterland-tunnelen

Hriks gate

NASJONAL-GALLERIET

IV's

Universitets-

Brasserie Paleo

Rosenkrantz

Pløens

Grubbe-gata

Møllergata

Torggata

gata

Storgata

Christian

Spectrum

Grønland

M

ontinental

Theatercaféen

gate

Grand Café

Karl

Dinner

Grand H.Oslo
by Scandic

Slottsgata

Brasserie
France

Johans

Stortorvet

DOMKIRKEN

Biskop Gunnerus' gate

Jernbanetorget

M

Maaemo

Stortingsgata

tdtjof

nsens
ass

Rosenkrantz

Akers-

Øvre

Wessels plass

Stortinget

Prinsens

gata

Olsens gate

Jernbane-torget

SENTRAL-STASJON

Schweigaards gate

Park Inn

Tollbu-

gate

gate

Strandgata

Comfort
H.Grand Central

Kongens

Christiana
torv

Statholderens
Mat og Vin Kjeller

Christian
Frederiks
plass

Rådhusgata

Rådhus-

Statholdergaarden

Opera

Brasserie Hansken

Kirke gata

Skipper

Vaaghals

AKERSHUS
FESTNING

Dronningens

Clarion Collection
H. Bastion

THE OSLO
OPERA HOUSE

Nodee
Barcode

estningen

MUSEET FOR
SAMTIDSKUNST

Festnings-tunnelen

BJØRVIKA

BISPEVIKA

RESISTANCE
MUSEUM

Akershusstranda

Kongens

Opera- tunnelen

3

C

D

▲ Hotel
● Restaurant

MAAEMO ❀❀❀

MODERN CUISINE • DESIGN • FASHIONABLE   XxX AC ⇌

Schweigaardsgate 15B ✉ 0191 – PLAN: D2
Ⓜ Grønland
TEL. 22 17 99 69 – **www**.maaemo.no
Closed 15-31 July, 23 December-8 January, 28 March-3 April, 16-18
May and Sunday-Tuesday

Menu 2800 NOK (dinner only and lunch Friday-Saturday)
(tasting menu only) (booking essential)

Chef:
Esben Holmboe Bang

Specialities:
Oyster emulsion with mussels and
dill. Reindeer with preserved plum
sauce and artichokes. Brown butter
ice cream, molasses and roasted
hazelnuts.

Maaemo means 'Mother Earth' and this striking restaurant is all about
connecting with nature. Service is perfectly choreographed and
dishes are brought down from the mezzanine feature kitchen and
finished at the table by the chefs themselves. Innovative, intricate
cooking awakens the senses with sublime flavour combinations –
some dishes take several days to construct.

GALT ❀

MODERN CUISINE • RUSTIC • CHIC   XX

Frognerveien 12B ✉ 0263 – PLAN: A2
TEL. 485 14 886 – **www**.galt.no
Closed 23 December-3 January, 31 March-3 April, Sunday and
Monday

Menu 795 NOK – Carte 530/650 NOK (dinner only)

Chef:
Bjørn Svensson

Specialities:
Langoustine, watercress emulsion
and fermented leeks. Halibut, onion
and lovage. Oat ice cream, praline
and crystallised chocolate.

The friends who previously ran Fauna and Oscarsgate have created
this warm, intimate restaurant with an appealingly rustic feel. The
set menu of 6 courses is nicely balanced, flavour combinations have
been well thought through, and the contrast in textures is a particular
strength.

KONTRAST ✿

SCANDINAVIAN • DESIGN • FASHIONABLE   XX   ᕃ   AC   ⇔

Maridalsveien 15 ✉ 0178 – PLAN: D1
TEL. 2160 0101 – **www**.restaurant-kontrast.no
Closed Christmas, New Year, Easter, 17 May, Sunday and Monday
Menu 950/1450 NOK – Carte 555/615 NOK (dinner only)

Chef:
Mikael Svensson

Specialities:
Tomatoes with pineapple weed gel and tagetes oil. Pork with elm seeds and Holtefjell XO cheese. Strawberries and meadowsweet.

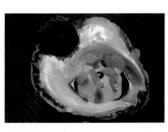

A modern restaurant with a stark, semi-industrial feel created by a concrete floor, exposed pipework and an open kitchen. Seasonal, organic Norwegian produce is used to create refined, original, full-flavoured dishes whose apparent simplicity often masks their complex nature. The service is well-paced.

STATHOLDERGAARDEN ✿

CLASSIC CUISINE • INTIMATE • ELEGANT   XxX   🕸   ⇔

Rådhusgata 11 (entrance on Kirkegata) ✉ 0151 – PLAN: C3
Ⓜ Stortinget
TEL. 22 41 88 00 – **www**.statholdergaarden.no
Closed 15 July-6 August, 23 December-3 January, 25 March-3 April, Sunday and bank holidays
Menu 975 NOK – Carte 925/1080 NOK (dinner only)
(booking essential)

Chef:
Bent Stiansen

Specialities:
Halibut with artichoke, sorrel, barley and lime sauce. Veal, sweetbreads, celeriac and morels. Norwegian raspberry, champagne and rose.

A charming 17C house in the city's heart. Three elegant rooms feature an array of antiques and curios, and have wonderfully ornate stucco ceilings hung with chandeliers. Expertly rendered classical cooking uses seasonal Norwegian ingredients in familiar combinations. Service is well-versed and willing.

RESTAURANTEIK 🎭

MODERN CUISINE • FASHIONABLE •
BRASSERIE   ✗✗ A/C ⬭

Clarion Collection H. Savoy - Universitetsgata 11 ✉ 0164 – **PLAN: C2**
Ⓜ National Theatret
TEL. 22 36 07 10 – **www**.restauranteik.no
Closed July, Easter, Christmas, Sunday and Monday
Menu 395 NOK (dinner only) (tasting menu only)

A contemporary L-shaped dining room set within a hotel close to the
National Gallery. It's minimalist in style, with colourful artwork, an
open kitchen and a glass-walled wine cellar. The weekly 3-5 course
set menu comprises inventive international cuisine. Service is efficient
and the atmosphere is friendly.

SMALHANS 🎭

TRADITIONAL CUISINE • NEIGHBOURHOOD •
SIMPLE   ✗ ⬭

Ullevålsveien 43 ✉ 0171 – **PLAN: C1**
TEL. 22 69 60 00 – **www**.smalhans.no
Closed 3 weeks July, Easter, Christmas and Monday
Menu 450 NOK (dinner) – Carte 320/490 NOK

A sweet neighbourhood café with friendly staff and an urban feel.
Coffee and homemade cakes are served in the morning, with a short
selection of dishes including soup and a burger on offer between
12pm and 4pm. A daily hot dish is available from 4-6pm, while set
menus and sharing plates are served at dinner.

À L'AISE ♨○

MODERN CUISINE • INTIMATE • ELEGANT

Essendrops gate 6 ✉ 0368 – PLAN: A1
Ⓜ Majorstuen
TEL. 21 05 57 00 – **www**.alaise.no
Closed 15 July-8 August, 9-17 April, Sunday and Monday
Menu 595 NOK (lunch) – Carte 895/1070 NOK (booking advisable)

This elegant, sophisticated restaurant is run by an engaging, knowledgeable team. The experienced chef is something of a Francophile: expect refined Gallic dishes packed with flavour and crafted from French and Norwegian produce.

ALEX SUSHI TJUVHOLMEN ♨○

SUSHI • SIMPLE • NEIGHBOURHOOD

Strandpromenaden 11 ✉ 0252 – PLAN: B3
TEL. 22 43 99 99 – **www**.alexsushi.no
Closed Easter, Christmas and Sunday
Menu 545/995 NOK (dinner) – Carte lunch 270/645 NOK

This simple neighbourhood restaurant sits in a fantastic harbourside spot and boasts a lovely heated terrace. The knowledgeable chefs skilfully prepare sushi, sashimi and nigiri at lunch, followed by 3 set menus at dinner.

ARAKATAKA ⁏◯

NORWEGIAN • FASHIONABLE • FRIENDLY   ✗ A/C ⇔

Mariboes gate 7 ✉ 0183 – **PLAN: D2**
Ⓜ Stortinget
TEL. 23 32 83 00 – **www**.arakataka.no
Closed July, Christmas-New Year and Easter

Menu 575 NOK – Carte 405/510 NOK (dinner only)
(booking advisable)

A smart glass-fronted restaurant with a central food bar, an open
kitchen and a buzzy atmosphere. Choose from a concise menu of
seasonal Norwegian small plates – they recommend 3 savoury dishes
plus a dessert per person.

BA 53 ⁏◯

MODERN CUISINE • FASHIONABLE •
NEIGHBOURHOOD   ✗✗ 🛜 A/C ⇔

Bygdoy Allé 53 ✉ 0265 – **PLAN: A2**
TEL. 21 42 05 90 – **www**.ba53.no
Closed July, Christmas, Easter and Sunday

Carte 380/540 NOK (dinner only)

A moody cocktail bar combines with a relaxed, softly lit brasserie
to create this stylish neighbourhood hotspot. Menus offer a mix of
Nordic classics and more modern dishes; four per person is ample.

BOKBACKA ⑪○

MODERN CUISINE • FASHIONABLE •
NEIGHBOURHOOD

XX ⇔

Skovveien 15 ⊠ 0257 – **PLAN: A2**
TEL. 412 60 144 – **www**.bokbacka.no
Closed Christmas, Easter, Sunday and Monday

Menu 795 NOK (dinner only) (tasting menu only)

A unique 'food bar' with clean, light styling and fun, idiosyncratic
features; most seats are arranged around the open kitchen, with only
4 other tables. Many of the theatrically presented dishes on the set
omakase-style menu have a story.

BON LIO ⑪○

MODERN CUISINE • SIMPLE • COSY

X

Fredensborgveien 42 ⊠ 0171 – **PLAN: C1**
TEL. 467 77 212 – **www**.bonlio.no
Closed Christmas, Easter, July, Sunday and Monday

Menu 795 NOK (dinner only) (surprise menu only)
(booking essential)

A lively, fun gastro-bar in a characterful 200 year old cottage. The
Norwegian owner grew up in Mallorca and showcases local and
imported ingredients in a surprise 12-17 course tapas-style menu.
Spanish beers and wines accompany.

BRASSERIE BLANCHE ⵏO

FRENCH • COSY • BRASSERIE

Josefinesgate 23 ✉ 0352 – **PLAN: B1**
TEL. 23 20 13 10 – **www**.blanche.no
Closed 9-31 July, 23-26 December and Monday
Menu 525 NOK – Carte 340/625 NOK (dinner only)

 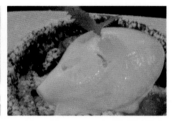

A cosy French restaurant housed in an 18C building which was originally a stable and later spent time as a garage and an interior furnishings store. It has a small front terrace, a bar decorated with wine boxes and a wall made of corks. The chef is a Francophile and creates flavoursome classic French dishes.

BRASSERIE FRANCE ⵏO

FRENCH • BRASSERIE • TRADITIONAL DÉCOR

Øvre Slottsgate 16 ✉ 0157 – **PLAN: C2**
Ⓜ Stortinget
TEL. 23 10 01 65 – **www**.brasseriefrance.no
Closed Easter, 23 December-2 January, Sunday and lunch Monday
Menu 395/550 NOK – Carte 435/700 NOK

This lively Gallic brasserie in a pedestrianised shopping street has several private dining rooms. Brasserie classics range from bouillabaisse to steak frites; for dessert, choose from the 'eat-as-much-as-you-like' pastry trolley.

BRASSERIE HANSKEN ⑩

MODERN CUISINE • FAMILY • BRASSERIE

Akersgate 2 ⊠ 0158 – PLAN: C2
Ⓜ Stortinget
TEL. 22 42 60 88 – **www**.brasseriehansken.no
Closed 1 week Easter, 1 week Christmas, Monday in July and Sunday
Menu 545/645 NOK – Carte 485/815 NOK

A delightfully traditional brasserie, centrally located by City Hall, with various charming dining areas and a fantastic terrace. Classical cooking follows the seasons and mixes French and Scandic influences; seafood is a speciality.

BRASSERIE PALEO ⑩

SCANDINAVIAN • DESIGN • BRASSERIE

Hotel Rosenkrantz • Rosenkrantz gate 1 ⊠ 0159 – PLAN: C2
Ⓜ National Theatrer
TEL. 23 31 55 80 – **www**.brasseriepaleo.no
Closed early July-early August, Christmas, Easter and Sunday
Carte 545/595 NOK

With a name which reflects its philosophy, and a contemporary urban style, this is not your typical hotel restaurant. Watch the chefs prepare attractive modern Scandinavian dishes in the open kitchen. Service is professional and friendly.

CRU ⠀⠀

NORWEGIAN • WINE BAR • TRENDY ⠀⠀ X 88

Ingelbrecht, Knudssøns gate 1 ⊠ 0365 – **PLAN: B1**
Ⓜ Majorstuen
TEL. 23 98 98 98 – **www**.cru.no
Closed 2 July-4 August, 22 December-4 January, Easter and Sunday
Menu 395 NOK – Carte 480/560 NOK (dinner only)

Upstairs, in the rustic restaurant, they serve a set 4 course menu with inventive British touches and 4 optional extra courses; while downstairs, in the wine bar, you can enjoy everything from nibbles to a full meal from the à la carte.

DINNER ⠀⠀

CHINESE • DESIGN • ELEGANT ⠀⠀ XX A/C ⟷

Stortingsgata 22 ⊠ 0161 – **PLAN: C2**
Ⓜ National Theatret
TEL. 23 10 04 66 – **www**.dinner.no
Closed 24 December-1 January and Sunday lunch
Menu 399/529 NOK – Carte 325/475 NOK

An intimate restaurant on the central square, close to the National Theatre. A black frosted glass façade masks a smart split-level interior. The kitchen focuses on Sichuan cuisine, with some artfully presented dim sum at lunch.

FEINSCHMECKER ¶O

TRADITIONAL CUISINE • CLASSIC DÉCOR •
NEIGHBOURHOOD   XxX 🕸 A/C ⇌

Balchens gate 5 ⊠ 0265 – **PLAN: A2**
TEL. 22 12 93 80 – **www**.feinschmecker.no
Closed 3 weeks summer, Christmas, Easter and Sunday
Menu 845 NOK – Carte 760/1015 NOK (dinner only)

This long-standing restaurant has a cosy, welcoming atmosphere and
a loyal local following, and is run by a charming team. The well-
presented dishes are classically based, with French influences. Wine
pairings are available.

FESTNINGEN ¶O

MODERN CUISINE • BRASSERIE •
FASHIONABLE   XX 🕸 ≼ ㅎ 🏠 A/C ⁴⁄₋ ⇌

Myntgata 9 ⊠ 0151 – **PLAN: C3**
TEL. 22 83 31 00 – **www**.festningenrestaurant.no
Closed 23 December-5 January, Easter and Sunday
Menu 315/595 NOK – Carte 615/855 NOK

A smart, contemporary brasserie with a terrace and lovely views
over the water to Aker Brygge; it was once a prison and its name
means 'fortress'. The experienced kitchen create unfussy, attractively
presented modern Nordic dishes using fresh local produce. The
impressive wine list is strong on burgundy.

FJORD 🍴

SEAFOOD • DESIGN • FASHIONABLE   ✗✗ [AC]

Kristian Augusts gt. 11 ✉ 0164 – **PLAN: C2**
Ⓜ National Theatret
TEL. 22 98 21 50 – **www**.restaurantfjord.no
Closed Christmas, Easter, Sunday and Monday

Menu 445/695 NOK (dinner only) (tasting menu only) (booking essential)

A contemporary restaurant opposite the National Gallery. Inside it's dimly lit, with an open kitchen, unusual cobalt blue walls and buffalo horns set into the chandeliers. The 3-6 course menu offers flavoursome seafood dishes.

FRU K 🍴

MODERN CUISINE • DESIGN • FASHIONABLE   ✗✗ ♿ [AC] 🚪 🚗

Thief Hotel • Landgangen 1 ✉ 0252 – **PLAN: B3**
TEL. 24 00 40 40 – **www**.thethief.com
Closed July, Christmas, Easter, Sunday and Monday

Menu 895 NOK (dinner only) (tasting menu only)

A chic hotel restaurant named after Fru Krogh, who tended animals on the Tjuvholmen peninsula long ago. Set 5 and 7 course menus use fine Norwegian ingredients to create tasty dishes; prime Norwegian seafood features highly.

GRAND CAFÉ ⅼO

MODERN CUISINE • CLASSIC DÉCOR •
VINTAGE

X 🥨 🛋 AC 🍴

Grand H.Oslo by Scandic • Karl Johans Gate 31 ✉ 0159 – PLAN: C2
Ⓜ Stortinget
TEL. 98 18 2000 – **www**.grandcafeoslo.no
Closed Easter and Christmas

Carte 425/585 NOK

This iconic restaurant dates from 1874; look out for the colourful mural
depicting past regulars including Edvard Munch and Henrik Ibsen.
The concise menu lists flavour-filled Nordic and international dishes.
The cellar wine bar opens Tues-Sat and offers snacks, charcuterie and
over 1,500 bottles of wine.

HAPPOLATI ⅼO

ASIAN • DESIGN • FRIENDLY

XX 🛋

St. Olavs Plass 2 ✉ 0165 – PLAN: C1
Ⓜ National Theatret
TEL. 479 78 087 – **www**.happolati.no
Closed 23 December-3 January, Easter, Sunday and Monday

Menu 525 NOK – Carte 385/455 NOK (dinner only)

This bright, modish restaurant fuses Asian and Nordic styles; its
assured cooking uses good quality ingredients and many dishes are
designed for sharing. Tightly packed tables and friendly service add
to the vibrant ambience.

HOS THEA ⓘO

ITALIAN • FAMILY • NEIGHBOURHOOD   XX

Gabels gate 11 ✉ 0272 – PLAN: A2
TEL. 22 44 68 74 – **www**.hosthea.no
Closed July, 24-26 December and 29 March-2 April

Carte 610/690 NOK (dinner only)

A small, well-established restaurant in a charming residential area. It's
decorated in natural hues and hung with beautiful oils. Menus offer
a concise selection of Mediterranean dishes; start with the delicious
homemade bread.

KOLONIALEN BISLETT ⓘO

MODERN CUISINE • BRASSERIE •
NEIGHBOURHOOD   X 🪑 AC

Sofiesgate 16 ✉ 0170 – PLAN: C1
TEL. 90 115 098 – **www**.kolonialenbislett.no
Closed last 3 weeks July, Sunday and bank holidays

Carte 350/560 NOK (booking essential at dinner)

Close to the stadium you'll find this cosy, modern bistro – previously
a grocer's shop for nearly 80 years. The concise, keenly priced menu
lists oysters, cured meats and wholesome Norwegian classics that
have been brought up-to-date.

LING LING ‖O

CANTONESE • FASHIONABLE

Stranden 30 ⊠ 0250 – **PLAN: B3**
TEL. 24 13 38 00 – **www**.lingling.hakkasan.com/oslo/
Closed 24-27 December, 1 January and Sunday
Menu 298/988 NOK – Carte 375/880 NOK

This more casual sister to Hakkasan offers an abbreviated menu of its signature Cantonese dishes but made using Norwegian produce. It has a great marina location, a cool lounge-bar and a terrific rooftop bar and terrace come summer.

LOFOTEN FISKERESTAURANT ‖O

SEAFOOD • BRASSERIE • SIMPLE

Stranden 75 ⊠ 0250 – **PLAN: B3**
TEL. 22 83 08 08 – **www**.lofotenfiskerestaurant.no
Closed Christmas
Menu 550 NOK – Carte 615/735 NOK

A traditional fjord-side restaurant hung with bright modern artwork and offering lovely views from its large windows and sizeable terrace. Watch as fresh, simply cooked fish and shellfish are prepared in the semi-open kitchen.

NODEE BARCODE ⭑○

ASIAN • FASHIONABLE • TRENDY

Dronning Eufemais gate 28 ✉ 0191 – PLAN: D3
Ⓜ Jernbanetorget
TEL. 22 93 34 50 – **www**.nodee.no
Closed 23 December–1 January and Sunday lunch
Menu 340/645 NOK – Carte 260/525 NOK

A moody, elegant restaurant serving an all-encompassing Asian menu featuring dim sum, sushi and dishes cooked on the Robata grill – crispy Peking duck is their speciality. There's a bar and terrace on the 13th floor and on the 14th floor is Nodee Sky, with its appealing set menu and city views.

OMAKASE BY ALEX CABIAO ⭑○

SUSHI • DESIGN

Ruseløkkveien 3, 1st floor ✉ 0251 – PLAN: B2
TEL. 456 85 022 – **www**.omakaseoslo.no
Closed Christmas, Easter, Sunday and bank holidays
Menu 1350 NOK (dinner only)

A three-sided counter with seats for 15 and two sittings per evening. The fish and shellfish come largely from Norwegian waters and the rice is American. The no-choice menu offers around 18 servings of Edomae-style sushi, although there can be surprises, like reindeer; some wine pairings are equally original.

PLAH ⅋○

THAI • NEIGHBOURHOOD • FRIENDLY   XX ⅋ 🚇 AIC ⇦

Hegdehaugsveien 22 ⊠ 0167 – PLAN: B1
TEL. 22 56 43 00 – **www**.plah.no
Closed 2 weeks July, Christmas, Easter and Sunday

Menu 595/795 NOK (dinner only) (tasting menu only)

Norwegian ingredients blend with Thai flavours at this well-run restaurant. Choose between two tasting menus: the 'Journey Through Thailand' or the 'Journey Through The Jungle' (vegetarian). Dishes are eye-catching, imaginative and full of flavour. Their neighbouring bar serves traditional Thai street food.

STATHOLDERENS MAT OG VIN KJELLER ⅋○

NORWEGIAN • RUSTIC • SIMPLE   X

Statholdergaarden • Rådhusgate 11
(entrance from Kirkegata) ⊠ 0151 – PLAN: C3
Ⓜ Stortinget
TEL. 22 41 88 00 – **www**.statholdergaarden.no
Closed July, 22 December-3 January, Sunday and bank holidays

Menu 650 NOK – Carte 715/940 NOK (dinner only) (booking essential)

The informal sister of Statholdergaarden – set over three rooms in the old vaults beneath it. One wall of the large entranceway is filled with wine bottles. Choose from a huge array of small plates or go for the 10 course tasting menu.

THEATERCAFÉEN

TRADITIONAL CUISINE • LUXURY • ROMANTIC

Continental Hotel • Stortingsgaten 24-26 ✉ 0117 - **PLAN: C2**
Ⓜ National Theatret
TEL. 22 82 40 50 - **www**.theatercafeen.no
Closed Christmas-New Year
Menu 395 NOK (lunch) - Carte 550/950 NOK

A prestigious Oslo institution in a grand hotel, this charming Viennese 'grand café' comes with pillars, black banquettes and art nouveau lighting. Fresh cakes and elaborate lunchtime sandwiches make way for ambitious dinners.

TJUVHOLMEN SJØMAGASINET

SEAFOOD • FASHIONABLE • BRASSERIE

Tjuvholmen Allé 14 ✉ 0251 - **PLAN: B3**
TEL. 23 89 77 77 - **www**.sjomagasinet.no
Closed Christmas, Easter, Sunday and bank holidays
Menu 355/675 NOK - Carte 585/795 NOK

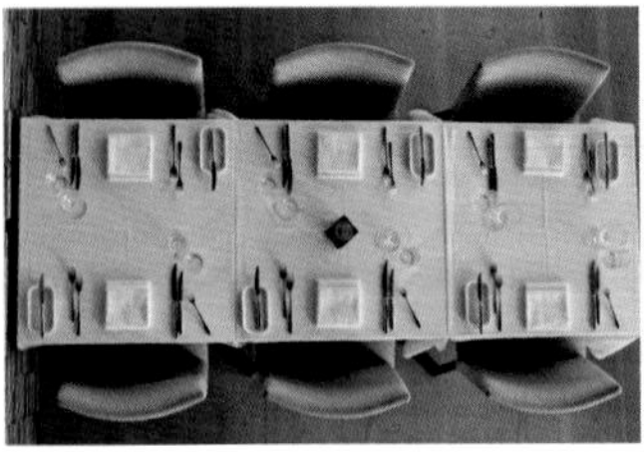

A vast restaurant with three dining rooms, a crab and lobster tank, a superb terrace and a wet fish shop. Its name means 'sea store' and menus are fittingly seafood based. Shellfish is from the nearby dock - the langoustines are fantastic.

VAAGHALS ⑩

SCANDINAVIAN • BRASSERIE •
FASHIONABLE   ✗ ♿ 🛜 AC 🍽

Dronning Eufemias gate 8 ✉ 0151 – **PLAN: D3**
Ⓜ Jernbanetorget
TEL. 920 70 999 – **www**.vaaghals.com
Closed last 3 weeks July, 22 December-3 January, Easter and
Sunday

Menu 695 NOK (dinner) – Carte 490/570 NOK

A bright, contemporary restaurant with an open kitchen and a terrace;
located on the ground floor of one of the modern 'barcode' buildings.
Scandinavian menus feature dry-aged meat; many of the dinner
dishes are designed for sharing.

CONTINENTAL

GRAND LUXURY • TRADITIONAL • CLASSIC

🏔 ♿ 🛗 AC 🧖 🚗

Stortingsgaten 24-26 ✉ 0117 – **PLAN: C2**
Ⓜ National Theatret
TEL. 22 82 40 00 – **www**.hotelcontinental.no
Closed Christmas-New Year

155 rm ⌐ – 👤 1995/3995 NOK 👥 2495/4500 NOK – 2 suites
THEATERCAFÉEN – See restaurant listing

A classic hotel situated by the National Theatre and run by the 4th
generation of the family, who ensure the service remains personal.
Bedrooms are stylish and contemporary – the corner suites have
balconies and views of the Royal Palace. Dine in the grand café or
from an inventive daily menu in Annen Etage.

GRAND H.OSLO BY SCANDIC

GRAND LUXURY · HISTORIC · ELEGANT

Karl Johans Gate 31 ⊠ 0159 – **PLAN: C2**
Ⓜ Stortinget
TEL. 23 21 20 00 – **www**.grand.no
274 rm ⊇ – ♦ 2080/3085 NOK ♦♦ 2280/3280 NOK – 5 suites
GRAND CAFÉ – See restaurant listing

An imposing, centrally located hotel built in 1874; the guest areas and grand ballrooms reflect this. Bedrooms are charming: some are modern, some are feminine and others are in a belle époque style. Dine on international fare in elegant Palmen or Nordic-inspired cooking in the Grand Café.

CLARION COLLECTION H. BASTION

BUSINESS · MODERN · PERSONALISED

Skippergata 5-7 ⊠ 0152 – **PLAN: C3**
Ⓜ Jernbanetorget
TEL. 22 47 77 00 – **www**.choicehotels.no
Closed Christmas-New Year and 23 March-3 April
99 rm ⊇ – ♦ 840/2935 NOK ♦♦ 990/3235 NOK – 5 suites

Two unassuming buildings house this boutique business hotel. The lounge has an English country house feel and an unusual collection of pictures and antiques are displayed throughout. Go for one of the newer, more characterful bedrooms. The small restaurant offers a complimentary one course supper.

CLARION COLLECTION H. GABELSHUS

TRADITIONAL • BUSINESS • CLASSIC

Gabelsgate 16 ✉ 0272 – **PLAN: A2**
TEL. 23 27 65 00 – **www**.nordicchoicehotels.no
Closed Easter and Christmas
114 rm ⌷ – ♦ 800/2240 NOK ♦♦ 940/2780 NOK – 1 suite

A beautiful ivy-covered house with a peaceful atmosphere, located in a smart residential neighbourhood. Charming bedrooms are a pleasing mix of traditional and designer styles. The classical wood-furnished lounge offers a complimentary one course supper in the evening.

COMFORT H. GRAND CENTRAL

CHAIN • BUSINESS • PERSONALISED

Jernbanetorget 1 ✉ 0154 – **PLAN: D2**
Ⓜ Jernbanetorget
TEL. 22 98 28 00 – **www**.comfortgrandcentral.no
170 rm ⌷ – ♦ 1420/1949 NOK ♦♦ 1610/2249 NOK

A great choice for businesspeople, this delightful hotel has a superb location above the main train station. Many of the soundproofed bedrooms have been individually styled and boast coordinating fabrics and colour schemes, as well as feature bathrooms. The restaurant offers a menu of simple Italian dishes.

OPERA

BUSINESS • MODERN • PERSONALISED

Dronning Eufemias gate 4 ✉ 0191 – PLAN: D2
Ⓜ Jernbanetorget
TEL. 24 10 30 00 – **www**.thonhotels.no/opera
Closed Christmas and New Year
480 rm ☲ – ♦ 1145/2705 NOK ♦♦ 1395/3055 NOK – 2 suites

Set on the doorstep of the National Library and the Opera House, this imposing hotel has a subtle theatrical theme both in its décor and the naming of its rooms. Bedrooms come in warm colours; ask for one at the front with a balcony. The Scala restaurant uses Norwegian produce in international recipes.

ROSENKRANTZ

BUSINESS • CHAIN • PERSONALISED

Rosenkrantz gate 1 ✉ 0159 – PLAN: C2
Ⓜ National Theatret
TEL. 23 31 55 00 – **www**.thonhotels.no
151 rm ☲ – ♦ 1395/3195 NOK ♦♦ 1695/3495 NOK – 8 suites
BRASSERIE PALEO – See restaurant listing

Located in the city centre and perfect for the business traveller. The brightly styled 8th floor guest lounge has complimentary drinks, snacks and light meals. Functional bedrooms come with Smart TVs and modern bathrooms.

THIEF

LUXURY • CONTEMPORARY • THEMED

Landgangen 1 ✉ 0252 – **PLAN: B3**
TEL. 24 00 40 00 – **www**.thethief.com
116 rm 🛏 – 👤 2790/5000 NOK 👫 2990/5500 NOK – 9 suites
FRU K – See restaurant listing

A smart hotel with a superb spa, located on a huge development on Thief Island. Works from global artists – including Andy Warhol – feature throughout. Facilities are state-of-the-art and a tablet controls all of the technology in the bedrooms. Dine on international dishes in Foodbar, which moves to the rooftop in summer, or seafood-focused tasting menus in Fru K.

PARK INN

BUSINESS • CHAIN • MINIMALIST

Ovre Slottsgate 2c ✉ 0157 – **PLAN: C2**
Ⓜ Stortinget
TEL. 22 40 01 00 – **www**.parkinn.com/hotel-oslo
118 rm 🛏 – 👤 995/3295 NOK 👫 1095/3395 NOK

A converted apartment block near Karl Johans Gate. Inside it's bright and modern with pleasant guest areas. Good-sized, functional bedrooms have pale wood furniture and modern lighting; the top floor rooms have balconies.

SAGA H. OSLO

TOWNHOUSE • HISTORIC • PERSONALISED

Eilert Sundstgate 39 ⊠ 0259 – **PLAN: B1**
TEL. 22 55 44 90 – **www**.sagahoteloslo.no
Closed Christmas and Easter
47 rm ☲ – 👤 995/2895 NOK 👥 1095/3495 NOK

A late Victorian townhouse with a smart, contemporary interior, set in a quiet city suburb. Most of the bedrooms are spacious: they have bold feature walls, modern facilities – including coffee machines – and small but stylish shower rooms. There's a Japanese restaurant in the basement.

SCANDIC VULKAN

BUSINESS • CHAIN • DESIGN

Maridalsveien 13 ⊠ 0178 – **PLAN: D1**
TEL. 21 05 71 00 – **www**.scandichotels.com/vulkan
Closed Christmas and Easter
149 rm ☲ – 👤 800/1800 NOK 👥 990/2200 NOK

A designer hotel set on the site of a former silver mine, next to a great food market. Modern bedrooms have bold feature walls and good facilities; the external-facing rooms have full-length windows. The bright, semi industrial style restaurant offers Italian-inspired dishes – in summer they only serve pizza.

Saga H. Oslo • Saga H. Oslo • Scandic Vulkan • Scandic Vulkan

SPECTRUM

BUSINESS • CHAIN • PERSONALISED

&

Brugata 7 ✉ 0186 – PLAN: D2
Ⓜ Grønland
TEL. 23 36 27 00 – **www**.thonhotels.no/spectrum
Closed Christmas
187 rm ⌂ – 👤 1575/2095 NOK 👥 1750/2695 NOK

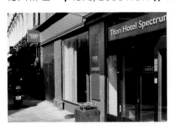

This unassuming looking hotel sits on a pedestrianised shopping
street, not far from the station. Bright, bold colours feature in a funky
interior and it has all the facilities a modern traveller needs; go for a
larger Business Room.

VIKA ATRIUM

BUSINESS • CHAIN • FUNCTIONAL

Munkedamsveien 45 ✉ 0250 – PLAN: B2
Ⓜ National Theatret
TEL. 22 83 33 00 – **www**.thonhotels.no
103 rm ⌂ – 👤 999/2045 NOK 👥 1195/2695 NOK

This busy business hotel is just minutes from Aker Brygge's
harbourside shops and restaurants, in a block containing a large
conference centre; some of the contemporary bedrooms overlook
the atrium. Breakfasts feature organic produce.

BEKKJARVIK GJESTGIVERI ⅋○

MODERN CUISINE • INN • CLASSIC DÉCOR   XX ⩽ P

Bekkjarvik Gjestgiveri Hotel • Bekkjarvik (Southwest: 14 km by Fv
546 and Fv 154) ✉ 5399
TEL. 55 08 42 40 – **www**.bekkjarvikgjestgiveri.no
Closed Christmas and New Year

Carte 635/950 NOK (bookings essential for non-residents)

A traditionally furnished restaurant in a family-owned and run hotel;
the sons are the ones behind the stoves. Choose 2, 3 or 7 dishes
from the menu. Classic cooking uses good quality ingredients and is
delivered with a modern hand.

BEKKJARVIK GJESTGIVERI   ⌂

TRADITIONAL • RURAL •

⩽ 佥 ⚒ P

Bekkjarvik (Southwest: 14 km by Fv 546 and Fv 154) ✉ 5399
TEL. 55 08 42 41 – **www**.bekkjarvikgjestgiveri.no
Closed Christmas and New Year

21 rm ☲ – ♦ 1690/1890 NOK ♦♦ 1790/2900 NOK
BEKKJARVIK GJESTGIVERI – See restaurant listing

Built by royal decree, this 17C hotel is delightfully located in a quiet
fishing port on the south of the island. Comfy, simply furnished
bedrooms are split between the original building and an annexe; the
latter have lovely harbour views.

LYSVERKET ⭐️🍴

MODERN CUISINE • DESIGN • FASHIONABLE   ✕✕ 🄰🄲 ⟷

Rasmus Meyers Allé 9 ✉ 5015
TEL. 55 60 3100 – **www**.lysverket.no
Closed 23 December-2 January, lunch during Easter, Sunday and
Monday
Menu 795 NOK (dinner) – Carte 565/665 NOK

This spacious, stylish restaurant is situated in a 1930s art museum
overlooking the park and offers an à la carte lunch and a set dinner
menu of 4 or 7 courses. Original modern dishes are made with quality
local ingredients.

RE-NAA ❀

CREATIVE • INTIMATE • ELEGANT   ✕✕

Steinkargata 10 (Breitorget) ✉ 4006
TEL. 51 55 1111 – **www**.restaurantrenaa.no
Closed mid July-mid August, Christmas-New Year, Easter
and Sunday-Tuesday
Menu 1400 NOK (dinner only) (tasting menu only) (booking
essential)

Chef:
Sven Erik Renaa

Specialities:
Cod with onion and caviar. Suckling
lamb in two servings. Rhubarb with
tarragon.

An appealing timber house in a quaint Old Town street houses this
elegant restaurant comprising 7 tables and an open kitchen. The
lengthy menu of up to 20 courses is a modern take on classic French
cooking. Ingredients are exceptional and their preparation precise;
flavours are distinct and superbly balanced.

SABI OMAKASE ❀

SUSHI • INTIMATE • FRIENDLY

XX

Pedersgata 38 ⊠ 4013
TEL. 918 26 823 – **www**.omakase.no
Closed Christmas, Easter and Sunday-Wednesday
Menu 1395 NOK (dinner only) (tasting menu only)
(booking essential)

Chef:
Roger Asakil Joya
Specialities:
Suimono. Nigiri. Seasonal ice
cream.

Sit at one of the ten seats at the counter to enjoy a multi-course sushi experience, with each course introduced and explained by the experienced chef-owner. Superlative Norwegian ingredients are prepared with exceptional skill and embellished with subtle modern touches. Sake or wine pairings accompany.

TANGO BAR & KJØKKEN ⊠○

MODERN CUISINE • SIMPLE

XX

Nedre Strandgate 23-25 ⊠ 4005
TEL. 51 50 12 30 – **www**.tango-bk.no
Closed Christmas, Easter, bank holidays and Sunday-Monday
Menu 750/1090 NOK (dinner only and Saturday lunch)
(tasting menu only) (booking essential)

Pleasantly located by the quayside, this smart restaurant is dominated by its open kitchen. The 3 course set menu offers a subtle modern interpretation of classic cooking and dishes are founded on good ingredients and sound techniques.

SWEDEN

E. Berthier/hemis.fr

DISTINCTIONS

STOCKHOLM

Sweden

Stockholm is the place to go for clean air, big skies and handsome architecture. And water. One of the great beauties of the city is the amount of water that runs through and around it; it's built on 14 islands, and looks out on 24,000 of them. An astounding two-thirds of the area within the city limits is made up of water, parks and woodland, and there are dozens of little bridges to cross to get from one part of town to another. It's little wonder Swedes appear so calm and relaxed. It's in Stockholm that the salty waters of the Baltic meet head-on the fresh waters of Lake Mälaren, reflecting the broad boulevards and

elegant buildings that shimmer along their edge. Domes, spires and turrets dot a skyline that in the summertime never truly darkens. The heart of the city is the Old Town, Gamla Stan, full of alleyways and lanes little changed from their medieval origins. Just to the north is the modern centre, Norrmalm: a buzzing quarter of shopping malls, restaurants and bars. East of Gamla Stan you reach the small island of Skeppsholmen, which boasts fine views of the waterfront; directly north from here is Östermalm, an area full of grand residences, while southeast you'll find the lovely park island of Djurgården. South and west of Gamla Stan are the two areas where Stockholmers particularly like to hang out, the trendy (and hilly) Södermalm, and Kungsholmen.

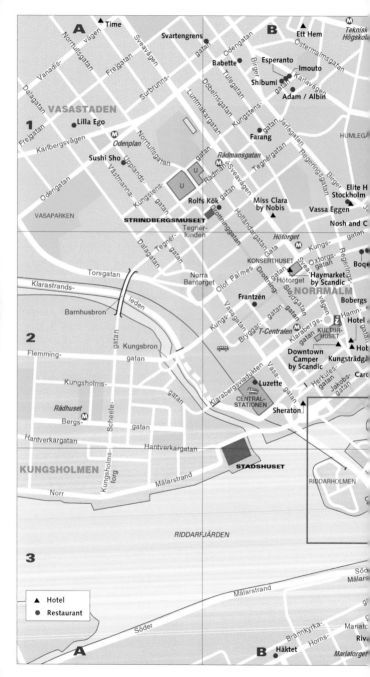

A ▲ Time

Norrtullsvägen

Vanadis-

Dalagatan

Sveavägen

Frejgatan

Surbrunns-

Vanadis-vägen

Svartengrens
gatan

Odengatan

Babette ●

Tulegatan

Döbelnsgatan

Luntmakargatan

Kungstens-

B ▲ Ett Hem

Östermalmsgatan

Birger Jarlsgatan

Esperanto
● Imouto
Shibumi ●
Adam / Albin

Karlavägen

Teknisk
Högskola Ⓜ

VASASTADEN

● Lilla Ego

Ⓜ Odenplan

Norrtullsgatan

Farang ●

gatan

Regeringsgatan

HUMLEG

Karlbergsvägen

Frejgatan

Sushi Sho ●

Ⓜ Odenplan

Upplands-

Västmanna-

Kungstens-

Rådmansgatan

Ⓜ Rådmansgatan

Svea vägen

Tegnérgatan

Birger Jarlsgatan

Elite H
Stockholm

Odengatan

VASAPARKEN

U

U

Rolfs Kök ●

Holländargatan

Drottninggatan

Miss Clara
by Nobis ▲

Vassa Eggen

STRINDBERGSMUSEET

Tegnér-
lunden

Nosh and C

gatan

Torsgatan

Dalagatan

Tegnérgatan

Norra
Bantorget

Olof Palmes Gata

Drottninggatan

Hötorget

Ⓜ Kungs-

KONSERTHUSET

Oxtorgsgatan

Regeringsg

Boq●

Klarastrands-

leden

Barnhusbron

Kungsbron

gatan

Frantzén ●

Vasagatan

Sveavägen

Hötorget ●

Sveavägen

Slöjdgatan

Haymarket
by Scandic

NORRMALM

Bobergs
Hotel

Flemming-

gatan

Kungsbron

gatan

Kungsgatan

Bryggargatan

T-Centralen Ⓜ

Klarabergsgatan

Vasagatan

ℹ Hamn-
KULTUR-
HUSET ▲ Hot

Kungshol-

Kungsholms-

Scheelegatan

Bergs-

gatan

Klarabergsviadukten

Vasa gatan

Downtown
Camper
by Scandic

Kungsträdgå

Herkules-
gatan

Jakobs-
gatan

Caro

Rådhuset Ⓜ

Hantverkargatan

Hantverkargatan

Luzette ●

CENTRAL-
STATIONEN

Sheraton

KUNGSHOLMEN

Kungsholms-
torg

Mälarstrand

STADSHUSET

RIDDARHOLMEN

Norr

RIDDARFJÄRDEN

3

Söd
Mälars

Mälarstrand

▲ Hotel
● Restaurant

Söder

Brännkyrka-

Horns-

Mariato

Riv

A

B ● Häktet

Mariatorget

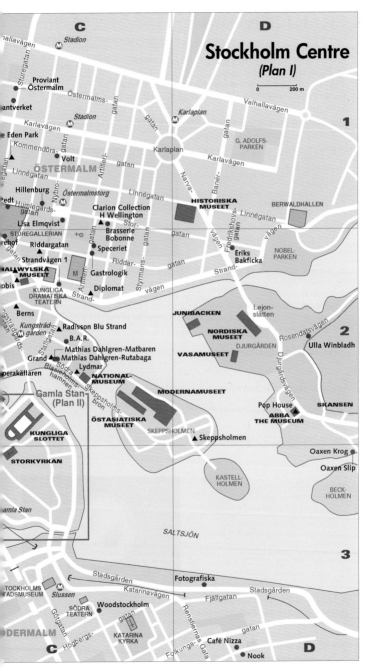

Stockholm Centre
(Plan I)

0   200 m

Stadion

hallavägen

Sturegatan

Proviant
Östermalm

antverket

Karlavägen

Östermalms-
gatan

Stadion

Karlaplan

Valhallavägen

G. ADOLFS-
PARKEN

e Eden Park

Kommendörs-

Volt

ÖSTERMALM

Linnégatan

Karlaplan

Karlavägen

gatan

gatan

Hillenburg

edt   Humlegårds-
gatan

Östermalmstorg

Nybro-

Linnégatan

Narva-

Banér-

HISTORISKA
MUSEET

BERWALDHALLEN

Linnégatan

Lisa Elmqvist

STUREGALLERIAN

Clarion Collection
H Wellington

Brasserie
Bobonne

vägen

rehof   Riddargatan

Strandvägen 1

Speceriet

Artilleri-
gatan

Stor-
gatan

Fredrikshovs-
gatan

Eriks
Bakficka

NOBEL-
PARKEN

MALLWYLSKA
MUSEET

obis

M

Gastrologik

Riddar-
gatan

Diplomat

Styrmans-
vägen

gatan

Strand

KUNGLIGA
DRAMATISKA
TEATERN

Berns

Strand-

Lejon-
slätten

Kungsträd-
gården

Radisson Blu Strand

JUNIBACKEN

NORDISKA
MUSEET

Rosendalsvägen

B.A.R.

Mathias Dahlgren-Matbaren

Grand   Mathias Dahlgren-Rutabaga

Lydmar

Södra
Blasieholms-
hamnen

VASAMUSEET

DJURGÅRDEN

Djurgårdsvägen

Ulla Winbladh

perakällaren

Gamla Stan
(Plan II)

NATIONAL-
MUSEET

Skeppsholms-
bron

MODERNAMUSEET

Pop House

ABBA
THE MUSEUM

SKANSEN

KUNGLIGA
SLOTTET

ÖSTASIATISKA
MUSEET

SKEPPSHOLMEN

Skeppsholmen

STORKYRKAN

Oaxen Krog

Oaxen Slip

amla Stan

KASTELL-
HOLMEN

BECK-
HOLMEN

SALTSJÖN

TOCKHOLMS
TADSMUSEUM

Stadsgården

Slussen

Katarinavägen

Woodstockholm

Fotografiska

Fjällgatan

Stadsgården

Renstiernas

SÖDRA
TEATERN

ÖDERMALM

Göta

Högbergs-

gatan

gatan

KATARINA
KYRKA

Gata

Folkunga

Café Nizza

gatan

Nook

CENTRE

FRANTZÉN ✿✿✿

MODERN CUISINE • DESIGN • FASHIONABLE XxX AK

Klara Norra Kyrkogata 26 ⊠ 111 22 – PLAN: B2
Ⓜ T-Centralen
TEL. 08-20 85 80 – www.restaurantfrantzen.com
Closed mid June-mid July, 2 weeks Christmas-New Year and
Sunday-Tuesday

Menu 3000 SEK (dinner only and lunch Friday-Saturday) (tasting
menu only) (booking essential)

Chef:
Björn Frantzén
Specialities:
Liquorice roasted calves' sweetbread. French toast 'Grand Tradition 2008'. Preserved blueberries, meringue, pepper and buffalo milk ice cream.

A unique restaurant set over 3 floors of a 19C property; ring the doorbell, enjoy an aperitif in the living room and visit the counter to have the day's luxurious ingredients explained. A beautiful wood counter borders the sleek kitchen and the chefs finish and explain the flavour-packed dishes at your table. Cooking is modern and creative but also uses classic techniques.

AGRIKULTUR ✿

MODERN CUISINE • COSY • NEIGHBOURHOOD X

Roslagsgatan 43 (Northwest: 2.5 km by Birger Jarlsgatan) ⊠ 113 54
TEL. 08-15 02 02 – www.agrikultur.se
Closed 5 weeks midsummer, 2 weeks Christmas-New Year and
Sunday-Monday

Menu 795 SEK (dinner only) (tasting menu only) (booking essential)

Chef:
Filip Fastén
Specialities:
Fish stock, fava beans and char. Langoustine and truffle. Apple, cardamom and maple syrup pie.

A lovely little restaurant with a certain homespun charm. The passionate young team deliver a 5 course menu which follows a local, seasonal and sustainable ethos. Creative cooking sees modernised Swedish classics prepared using some more traditional methods and the Aga and wood-burning oven play a key part.

EKSTEDT ✿

MEATS AND GRILLS • DESIGN • FRIENDLY 🍴 ⚉ ⅋

Humlegårdsgatan 17 ⊠ 114 46 – PLAN: C1
Ⓜ Östermalmstorg
TEL. 08-611 12 10 – **www**.ekstedt.nu
Closed 24, 25 and 31 December, midsummer, Sunday and Monday
Menu 890/1090 SEK (dinner only) (tasting menu only) (booking essential)

Chef:
Niklas Ekstedt

Specialities:
Blackened leeks with vendace roe and charcoal-smoked cream. Pike-perch, chanterelles and peas. Wood-fired honey cake with raspberries.

An unassuming façade hides a very relaxed, friendly, yet professionally run brasserie, where ingredients are cooked in a wood-burning oven, over a fire-pit or smoked through a chimney using birch wood. Dishes are inventive but well-balanced – they are given their finishing touches at the stone bar.

ESPERANTO ✿

CREATIVE • FASHIONABLE • DESIGN 🍴🍴🍴 A/C

Kungstensgatan 2 (1st Floor) ⊠ 114 25 – PLAN: B1
Ⓜ Tekniska Högskolan
TEL. 08-696 23 23 – **www**.esperantorestaurant.se
Closed July, Christmas, Easter and Sunday-Tuesday
Menu 1450/1900 SEK (dinner only) (tasting menu only)

Chef:
Sayan Isaksson

Specialities:
Oyster with sugar snap peas and blossoms. Guinea fowl egg, autumn vegetables and goat's milk yoghurt. Sunchoke pancake, maple butter and frozen milk.

Esperanto is a language that crosses frontiers, as does this restaurant's food. Passionately prepared, original Swedish and Asian dishes have a theatrical element, which is fitting seeing as it's located in a 1920s theatre. The modern room has a silver vaulted ceiling and all tables face the open kitchen.

GASTROLOGIK ✿

WORLD CUISINE • INTIMATE • DESIGN

XX ✿

Artillerigatan 14 ⊠ 114 51 – PLAN: C2
Ⓜ Östermalmstorg
TEL. 08-662 30 60 – **www**.gastrologik.se
Closed Christmas-New Year, midsummer weekend, Sunday and
Monday

Menu 1595 SEK (dinner only) (surprise menu only) (booking
essential)

Chef:
Jacob Holmström and Anton
Bjuhr

Specialities:
Grilled langoustine and potato
pancake with herbs. Roasted quail
with miso and truffle butter. Wild
camomile with sorrel ice cream and
rhubarb.

This intimate restaurant is owned by two accomplished young chefs.
Cooking is innovative, flavours are pure and each main ingredient
is allowed to shine. Dishes rely on the latest seasonal ingredients to
arrive at the door, so are constantly evolving; the menu isn't presented
to you until the end of the meal.

IMOUTO ✿

SUSHI • INTIMATE • SIMPLE

X A/C

Kungstensgatan 2 (1st Floor) ⊠ 114 25 – PLAN: B1
Ⓜ Tekniska Högskolan
TEL. 08-696 23 23 – **www**.imouto.se
Closed July, Christmas, Easter and Sunday-Tuesday

Menu 1200 SEK (dinner only) (booking essential)

Specialities:
Soy-glazed langoustine. Turbot
with wild garlic oil. Pike-perch
sushi.

Its name means 'little sister' and you'll find this 9-seater sushi counter
in the corner of Esperanto restaurant. Only an omakase menu is
offered, with hot and cold dishes served before the sushi; the rice is
from Japan but the fish is mainly from Swedish waters. There are two
sittings on Fridays and Saturdays.

MATHIAS DAHLGREN-MATBAREN ✿

MODERN CUISINE • FASHIONABLE • DESIGN ✗ &. A/C

Grand Hotel • Södra Blasieholmshamnen 6 ⊠ 103 27 – PLAN: C2
Ⓜ Kungsträdgården
TEL. 08-679 35 00 – **www**.mdghs.com
Closed 13 July-6 August, 22 December-7 January, Saturday lunch
and Sunday

Carte 475/835 SEK (booking advisable)

Specialities:
Squid with trout roe, artichoke
and soy. Chargrilled pork, truffle,
cabbage and hazelnuts. Yuzu
sabayon with Swedish berries
and sponge cake.

This popular hotel restaurant is both fun and charmingly run. The
open kitchen specialises in flavoursome, well-balanced dishes from an
appealing menu divided into the headings 'From our country', 'From
other countries' or 'From the plant world'. They keep some seats at
the counter for those who haven't booked.

OPERAKÄLLAREN ✿

CLASSIC CUISINE • LUXURY • HISTORIC XXXXX 🐌 💿

Operahuset, Karl XII's Torg ⊠ 111 86 – PLAN: C2
Ⓜ Kungsträdgården
TEL. 08-676 58 01 – **www**.operakallaren.se
Closed 23 December -15 January, July, midsummer, Sunday and
Monday

Menu 1050/1550 SEK (dinner only) (booking advisable)

Specialities:
Spider crab ravioli, parsley
emulsion and crab velouté. Butter-
baked sole with truffle and lobster.
Blackcurrant bavarois and sorrel
ice cream.

Sweden's most opulent restaurant sits within the historic Opera
House, and the stunning, high-ceilinged room boasts original gilt
panelling decorated with frescoes and carvings. Carefully constructed
dishes are underpinned by classic techniques. The wine list boasts
extensive vintages of the world's great wines.

SUSHI SHO ✿

JAPANESE • NEIGHBOURHOOD • FRIENDLY

Upplandsgatan 45 ✉ 113 28 – PLAN: A1
Ⓜ Odenplan
TEL. 08-30 30 30 – **www**.sushisho.se
Closed Christmas, New Year, July, midsummer, Sunday and Monday
Menu 695 SEK (dinner only and Saturday lunch) (surprise menu only) (booking essential)

Chef:
Carl Ishizaki
Specialities:
Seared halibut skirt with bonito vinegar. Herring with akazu shari. Soy-cured egg yolk with tuna, toasted rice and okra.

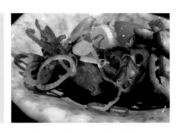

With its white tiled walls and compact counter seating the room couldn't be simpler, but the food is sublime. Meals are served omakase-style, with the chef deciding what's best each day and dishes arriving as they're ready. Top quality seafood from local waters features alongside some great egg recipes.

VOLT ✿

CREATIVE • INTIMATE • NEIGHBOURHOOD

Kommendörsgatan 16 ✉ 114 48 – PLAN: C1
Ⓜ Stadion
TEL. 08-662 34 00 – **www**.restaurangvolt.se
Closed 4 weeks summer, Christmas, New Year and Sunday-Monday
Menu 685/885 SEK (dinner only) (booking essential)

Chef:
Peter Andersson and Fredrik Johnsson
Specialities:
Zucchini with scallions and sour milk. Pike-perch with Jerusalem artichoke and seaweed. Strawberries with wild camomile.

An intimate, welcoming restaurant run by a young but experienced team. Cooking is natural in style, with the largely organic produce yielding clear, bold flavours – natural wines also feature. Ingredients are arranged in layers, so that each forkful contains a little of everything; choose 4 or 6 courses.

BRASSERIE BOBONNE 😨

FRENCH • COSY • BISTRO   ✗

Storgatan 12 ✉ 114 51 – PLAN: C1
Ⓜ Östermalmstorg
TEL. 08-660 03 18 – **www**.bobonne.se
Closed 4 weeks summer, Christmas and Sunday
Menu 550 SEK (dinner) – Carte 320/655 SEK

This sweet neighbourhood restaurant has a warm, homely feel, and
the owners proudly welcome their guests from the open kitchen.
Modern artwork hangs on the walls and contrasts with traditional
features such as mosaic tiling. Classic cooking has a French core and
dishes show obvious care in their preparation.

EAT 😨

ASIAN • BRASSERIE • FASHIONABLE   ✗ ♿ 🏛

Jakobsbergsgatan 15 ✉ 111 44 – PLAN: B2
Ⓜ Hötorget
TEL. 08-509 203 00 – **www**.eatrestaurant.se
Closed Christmas-New Year, mid July-mid August, Saturday
lunch and Sunday
Menu 265 SEK (lunch) – Carte 330/550 SEK (bookings advisable at
dinner)

Pass the EAT 'Market' fast food outlet in this upmarket shopping mall
and head for the Oriental 'Bistro' with its rich, moody colour scheme
and central cocktail bar. The name stands for 'European Asian Taste'
and the Chinese dishes are flavoursome, well-executed and designed
for sharing.

LILLA EGO ☺

MODERN CUISINE • BISTRO • FRIENDLY   🍴 ⛶

Västmannag 69 ✉ 113 26 – **PLAN: A1**
Ⓜ Odenplan
TEL. 08-27 44 55 – **www**.lillaego.com
Closed July, Christmas, New Year, Easter, midsummer, Sunday and
Monday

Carte 465/675 SEK (dinner only) (booking essential)

Still one of the hottest tickets in town, Lilla Ego comes with a pared-
down look and a buzzy vibe; if you haven't booked, try for a counter
seat. The two modest chef-owners have created an appealingly priced
menu of robust seasonal dishes. The 'wrestling' sausage will challenge
even the biggest of appetites.

PROVIANT ÖSTERMALM ☺

SWEDISH • BISTRO • INTIMATE   🍴 ♿ 🏠

Sturegatan 19 ✉ 114 36 – **PLAN: C1**
Ⓜ Stadion
TEL. 08-22 60 50 – **www**.proviant.se
Closed 3 weeks July, 2 weeks Christmas, 1 January and lunch
Saturday-Sunday

Menu 295/625 SEK – Carte 455/625 SEK

A lively restaurant boasting smart, contemporary décor, a small
counter and an adjoining foodstore; located in a chic residential area
by Sture Park. Swedish ingredients feature highly – choose from
rustic, classically based dishes on the blackboard, a French-inspired
à la carte or the house specialities.

ROLFS KÖK 🕮

MODERN CUISINE • BISTRO • RUSTIC   🍴 🏵

Tegnérgatan 41 ✉ 111 61 – PLAN: B1
Ⓜ Rådmansgatan
TEL. 08-10 16 96 – **www**.rolfskok.se
Closed July, 24-25 and 31 December, 1 January, midsummer
and lunch Saturday-Sunday

Menu 148 SEK (lunch) – Carte dinner 505/665 SEK (booking
essential)

A popular, buzzy restaurant in a lively commercial district, run by a
passionate chef-owner. The contemporary interior was designed by
famous Swedish artists; sit at the counter to watch the chefs in action.
Dishes include homely Swedish classics and blackboard specials –
every dish has a wine match.

SHIBUMI 🕮

JAPANESE • MINIMALIST • FASHIONABLE   🍴 A/C

Kungstensgatan 2 ✉ 114 25 – PLAN: B1
Ⓜ Tekniska Högskolan
TEL. 08-696 23 10 – **www**.shibumi.se
Closed Christmas, New Year, Easter, midsummer, Sunday and
Monday

Carte 225/405 SEK (dinner only) (booking advisable)

This moody, modern restaurant is based on a Japanese izakaya.
It's open until late and comes with an underground buzz – and not
just because it's in a basement. The menu offers authentic dishes
designed for sharing; some with a slightly westernised edge. The daily
changing cocktail list is worth a look.

ADAM / ALBIN ⑪○

MODERN CUISINE • INTIMATE • NEIGHBOURHOOD   ⑂ &
Ⓐⓒ

Rådmansgatan 16 ✉ 114 25 – PLAN: B1
Ⓜ Tekniska Högskolan
TEL. 08-411 55 35 – **www**.adamalbin.se
Closed Christmas, Sunday, bank holidays and restricted opening in
summer
Menu 895 SEK (dinner only) (booking essential)

Owners Adam and Albin have stamped their mark on this charming
restaurant, which comes with Italian marble clad walls and a mix of
individual and communal tables. Snacks are followed by a 4 course
menu, where refined, eye-catching dishes blend the ethos of a
Scandic kitchen with Asian flavours.

AG ⑪○

MEATS AND GRILLS • RUSTIC • FASHIONABLE   ⑂⑂ ⑧ Ⓐⓒ

Kronobergsgatan 37 (2nd Floor), Kungsholmen
(via Flemminggatan) ✉ 112 33
Ⓜ Fridshemsplan
TEL. 08-410 68 100 – **www**.restaurangag.se
Closed July, 24-25 and 31 December, 1 January and Sunday
Carte 425/805 SEK (dinner only)

An industrial, New York style eatery on the 2nd floor of an old silver
factory. Swedish, American and Scottish beef is displayed in huge
cabinets and you choose your accompaniments. Expect a great wine
list and smooth service.

BABETTE ⅼ❍

MODERN CUISINE • NEIGHBOURHOOD • BISTRO ✗ 🏠

Roslagsgatan 6 ✉ 113 55 – **PLAN: B1**
Ⓜ Tekniska Högskolan
TEL. 08-509 022 24 – **www**.babette.se
Closed 24-26, 31 December and 18-25 June

Carte 295/415 SEK (dinner only)

You'll feel at home in this modern neighbourhood bistro. Cooking is rustic and unfussy and the daily selection of small plates and pizzas makes dining flexible. They limit their bookings so that they can accommodate walk-ins.

B.A.R. ⅼ❍

SEAFOOD • BRASSERIE • FASHIONABLE ✗ AC

Blasieholmsgatan 4a ✉ 111 48 – **PLAN: C2**
Ⓜ Kungsträdgården
TEL. 08-611 53 35 – **www**.restaurangbar.se
Closed Christmas-New Year, Saturday lunch and Sunday

Carte 345/585 SEK

This bright, buzzy restaurant is just a cast away from the waterfront and has a semi-industrial fish-market style. Choose your seafood from the fridge or the tank, along with a cooking style, a sauce and one of their interesting sides.

BOBERGS ⅊◯

MODERN CUISINE • ELEGANT •
CLASSIC DÉCOR   ✗✗✗ ⅊ A/C

NK Department Store (4th floor), Hamngatan 18-20 ✉ 111 47 – PLAN: B2
Ⓜ Kungsträdgården
TEL. 08-762 81 61 – **www**.bobergsmatsal.se
Closed July-mid August, Christmas-New Year, Sunday and bank
holidays

Menu 345 SEK – Carte 395/765 SEK (lunch only) (booking advisable)

Head past the canteen in this historic department store to the elegant
birch-panelled room and ask for a river view. Choose the set business
lunch or from the seasonal à la carte; classic cooking mixes French
and Swedish influences.

BOQUERIA ⅊◯

SPANISH • TAPAS BAR • FASHIONABLE   ✗ ⅊ ☷

Jakobsbergsgatan 17 ✉ 111 44 – PLAN: B2
Ⓜ Hötorget
TEL. 08-30 74 00 – **www**.boqueria.se
Closed 24-25 December, 1 January and midsummer

Menu 145 SEK (weekday lunch) – Carte 370/995 SEK

A vibrant, bustling tapas restaurant with high-level seating, located
in a smart mall. Appealing menus offer tapas and a range of authentic
dishes for two or more to share. Sangria and pintxos can be enjoyed
in their nearby bar.

CAROUSEL ⅋○

SWEDISH • CLASSIC DÉCOR • HISTORIC

Gustav Adolfs Torg 20 ✉ 111 53 – **PLAN: B2**
Ⓜ Kungsträdgården
TEL. 08-10 27 57 – **www**.restaurantcarousel.se
Closed Christmas, midsummer and Sunday

Carte 425/765 SEK

Start with a drink under the impressive original ceiling in the bar then sit near the carousel or out on the terrace. The experienced chefs carefully prepare flavoursome dishes which follow the seasons and have classic Swedish roots.

ERIKS BAKFICKA ⅋○

SWEDISH • BISTRO

Fredrikshovsgatan 4 ✉ 115 23 – **PLAN: D2**
TEL. 08-660 15 99 – **www**.eriks.se
Closed July, Christmas, Easter, Saturday lunch and Sunday

Carte 445/780 SEK

Set in a residential area close to Djurgårdsbron Bridge and a favourite with the locals. The bistro-style interior has wood panelling and marble-topped tables. Simple, unpretentious cooking features Swedish classics and a 'dish of the day'.

FARANG ⫞◎

SOUTH EAST ASIAN • MINIMALIST •
FASHIONABLE

XX &. A/C

Tulegatan 7 ⊠ 113 53 – PLAN: B1
Ⓜ Rådmansgatan
TEL. 08-673 74 00 – **www**.farang.se
Closed July, Christmas, Sunday and Monday
Menu 245/695 SEK – Carte 410/655 SEK

The unusual front door harks back to its Stockholm Electric Company
days, and behind it lies a stylish restaurant and bar – the former sits
in the old machine hall. Zingy, aromatic dishes focus on Southeast
Asia and are full of colour.

HANTVERKET ⫞◎

MODERN CUISINE • RUSTIC • FASHIONABLE

XX 😷 A/C

Sturegatan 15 ⊠ 114 36 – PLAN: C1
Ⓜ Stadion
TEL. 08-121 32160 – **www**.restauranghantverket.se
Closed 3 weeks July, Christmas, Saturday lunch and Sunday
Menu 295 SEK (lunch) – Carte 300/525 SEK (booking advisable)

Exposed ducting contrasts with chunky tables and leafy plants at this
buzzy restaurant. It has a cool lounge-bar, counter seats and a mix
of raised and regular tables. Cooking has an artisanal Swedish heart
and service is bright and breezy.

HILLENBERG ⅃⃝

MODERN CUISINE • DESIGN • BRASSERIE

Humlegårdsgatan 14 ⊠ 114 34 – PLAN: C1
Ⓜ Östermalmstorg
TEL. 08-519 42 153 – **www**.hillenberg.se
Closed Christmas and Sunday

Carte 365/860 SEK

There's a marble bar on each side of this bright, modern restaurant, where the designer's eye for detail is evident. The food reflects the surroundings by being fresh, contemporary, colourful and free from unnecessary frills.

LISA ELMQVIST ⅃⃝

SEAFOOD • FAMILY • BISTRO

Humlesgårdsgatan 1 ⊠ 114 39 – PLAN: C1
Ⓜ Östermalmstorg
TEL. 08-553 404 10 – **www**.lisaelmqvist.se
Closed 24 December, midsummer, Sunday and bank holidays

Carte 425/1190 SEK

While the original 19C market hall is being restored, this established family-run restaurant is operating from the temporary marketplace next door. Top quality seafood from the day's catch features in unfussy, satisfying combinations.

LUZETTE 🍴

SWEDISH • BRASSERIE • DESIGN

Centralstationen, Centralplan 25 ⌧ 111 20 – PLAN: B2
Ⓜ T-Centralen
TEL. 08-519 316 00 – **www**.luzette.se
Carte 425/715 SEK

A modern brasserie in the Central train station, inspired by the grand restaurants of old; its name means 'light' and refers to the 1920s luminaire designed by Peter Behrens. Swedish menus include weekend brunches and rotisserie specials.

MATHIAS DAHLGREN-RUTABAGA 🍴

VEGETARIAN • SIMPLE • FASHIONABLE

Grand Hotel • Södra Blasieholmshamnen 6 ⌧ 103 27 – PLAN: C2
Ⓜ Kungsträdgården
TEL. 08-679 35 84 – **www**.mdghs.se
Closed 22 December-7 January, 13 July-6 August and Sunday
Menu 795 SEK – Carte 260/375 SEK (dinner only) (booking essential)

A light, bright restaurant offering something one doesn't usually find in grand hotels – vegetarian cuisine. The sharing plates come with flavours from across the world; the 'Taste of Rutabaga' menu best showcases the kitchen's range.

NOSH AND CHOW †O

INTERNATIONAL • BRASSERIE • FASHIONABLE ✗✗ ♿ AC ⇌

Norrlandsgatan 24 ✉ 111 43 – PLAN: B2
Ⓜ Hötorget
TEL. 08-503 389 60 – **www**.noshandchow.se
Closed Easter, 24 December, 1 January, midsummer and Sunday
Menu 295/450 SEK – Carte 345/785 SEK

This former bank has been transformed into a glitzy cocktail bar and brasserie which displays a smart mix of New York and New England styling. Filling dishes blend French, American and Swedish influences with other global flavours.

SPECERIET †O

CLASSIC CUISINE • SIMPLE ✗ AC

Artillerigatan 14 ✉ 114 51 – PLAN: C2
Ⓜ Östermalmstorg
TEL. 08-662 30 60 – **www**.speceriet.se
Closed July-August, Christmas-New Year, midsummer, Saturday lunch, Sunday-Monday and bank holidays
Carte 375/575 SEK

The more casual addendum to the Gastrologik restaurant will get you in the mood for sharing. Sit at communal tables and choose from three main dishes at lunchtime and a wider selection of mix and match dishes at dinner.

STRANDVÄGEN 1 🍴

INTERNATIONAL • DESIGN • ELEGANT   ✕✕ 🛖 A/C

Strandvägen 1 ✉ 114 51 – **PLAN: C2**
Ⓜ Kungsträdgården
TEL. 08-663 80 00 – **www**.strandvagen1.se
Closed 24 December
Carte 425/765 SEK

Sit on the terrace of this modern bistro-style restaurant – a former
bank – and watch the boats bobbing up and down in the harbour.
Seasonal menus offer generously proportioned, globally inspired
dishes with bold flavours.

STUREHOF 🍴

SEAFOOD • BRASSERIE • FASHIONABLE   ✕ 🎴 ♿ 🛖 A/C ⟷

Stureplan 2 ✉ 114 46 – **PLAN: C2**
Ⓜ Östermalmstorg
TEL. 08-440 57 30 – **www**.sturehof.com
Carte 290/915 SEK

This bustling city institution dates back over a century and is a
wonderful mix of the traditional and the modern. It boasts a buzzing
terrace, several marble-topped bars and a superb food court. Classic
menus focus on seafood.

SVARTENGRENS ⅋O

MEATS AND GRILLS • FRIENDLY • NEIGHBOURHOOD ✗

Tulegatan 24 ✉ 113 53 – PLAN: B1
Ⓜ Tekniska Högskolan
TEL. 08-612 65 50 – **www**.svartengrens.se
Closed midsummer and Christmas
Menu 725 SEK – Carte 315/845 SEK (dinner only)

The eponymous chef-owner has created a modern bistro specialising in sustainable meat and veg from producers in the archipelago. Along with smoking and pickling, the dry-ageing is done in-house, and the cuts change daily.

VASSA EGGEN ⅋O

MEATS AND GRILLS • FASHIONABLE • RUSTIC ✗✗ A/C

Elite H. Stockholm Plaza • Birger Jarlsgatan 29 ✉ 103 95 – PLAN: B1
Ⓜ Östermalmstorg
TEL. 08-21 61 69 – **www**.vassaeggen.com
Closed midsummer, Christmas, Saturday lunch and Sunday
Menu 695 SEK – Carte 495/1000 SEK

A pleasant bar leads through to a dimly lit hotel dining room where bold artwork hangs on the walls. Hearty Swedish cooking relies on age-old recipes, with a particular focus on meat; whole beasts are butchered and hung on-site.

GRAND

LUXURY • HISTORIC BUILDING • ELEGANT

Södra Blasieholmshamnen 6 ⊠ 103 27 – PLAN: C2
Ⓜ Kungsträdgården
TEL. 08-679 35 00 – **www**.grandhotel.se
278 rm ⌑ – ♦ 3600/4200 SEK ♦♦ 4900/5800 SEK – 34 suites
MATHIAS DAHLGREN-MATBAREN ✿ – See restaurant listing
MATHIAS DAHLGREN-RUTABAGA – See restaurant listing

The Grand certainly lives up to its name with its Corinthian columns, handsome panelled bar and impressive spa. Classical bedrooms have marble-decked bathrooms and those at the front have great views over the water to the Old Town. Dining choices include Verandan with its harbour outlook and smörgåsbords, lively Matbaren and vegetarian restaurant Rutabaga.

HOTEL AT SIX

BUSINESS • DESIGN • CONTEMPORARY

Brunkebergstorg 6 ⊠ 111 51 – PLAN: B2
Ⓜ Kungsträdgården
TEL. 08-578 828 00 – **www**.hotelatsix.com
340 rm – ♦ 1700/2400 SEK ♦♦ 1700/2400 SEK, ⌑ 175 SEK – 1 suite

With its laid-back vibe, bold colour scheme, contemporary art collection and 14m long cocktail bar and 'listening lounge', its cool interior couldn't be more of a contrast to its unassuming façade. Bedrooms are monochrome; those on the top floors have panoramic windows. The modern brasserie serves global fare.

NOBIS

HISTORIC • DESIGN • PERSONALISED

Norrmalmstorg 2-4 ⊠ 111 86 – PLAN: C2
Ⓜ Östermalmstorg
TEL. 08-614 10 00 – **www**.nobishotel.com
201 rm – ♦ 1890/2290 SEK ♦♦ 2290/2990 SEK, ☕ 175 SEK – 1 suite

It started life as two Royal Palaces and later became a bank (the famous 'Stockholm Syndrome' robbery took place here); now it's a smart hotel with two internal courtyards and spacious bedrooms with clean lines, African wood furnishings and marble bathrooms. Dine on refined Italian cuisine in Caina or more rustic, wholesome dishes in Bakfica, with its pavement terrace.

SHERATON

BUSINESS • CHAIN • MODERN

Tegelbacken 6 ⊠ 101 23 – PLAN: B2
Ⓜ T-Centralen
TEL. 08-412 36 02 – **www**.sheratonstockholm.com
465 rm – ♦ 1395/5185 SEK ♦♦ 1395/5185 SEK, ☕ 259 SEK – 29 suites

This was the first Sheraton to open in Europe, back in 1971, and its unassuming concrete façade is now a listed feature. Bedrooms are smart, spacious and understated, and some overlook Lake Mälaren or the Old Town. The lively restaurant offers international buffet lunches and traditional Swedish dinners.

BERNS

HISTORIC BUILDING • BOUTIQUE HOTEL • DESIGN

Näckströmsgatan 8, Berzelii Park ✉ 111 47 - **PLAN: C2**
Ⓜ Kungsträdgården
TEL. 08-566 322 00 - **www**.berns.se
82 rm - 1100/3300 SEK 1200/3500 SEK, 195 SEK - 6 suites

In 1863 Heinrich Robert Berns opened Stockholm's biggest concert and party hall on this site and, continuing that tradition, events are a big part of this hotel's business. Bedrooms are modern and some have seating areas or balconies. The stunning rococo ballroom offers an extensive Asian fusion menu.

DIPLOMAT

TRADITIONAL • LUXURY • ELEGANT

Strandvägen 7C ✉ 114 56 - **PLAN: C2**
Ⓜ Kungsträdgården
TEL. 08-459 68 00 - **www**.diplomathotel.com
130 rm - 2550/3950 SEK 2850/4650 SEK - 3 suites

Early 20C charm combines with modern furnishings in this art nouveau hotel. Take the old cage lift up to the cosy library, which leads through to a sweet little cocktail bar. Elegant bedrooms come in pastel hues and some have harbour views. T Bar (the old tea salon) serves Scandinavian-inspired brasserie dishes.

DOWNTOWN CAMPER BY SCANDIC 🏚️

BUSINESS • INDUSTRIAL • ECO-FRIENDLY

⛺ ♿ 🛄 🆒 🎐 AC ⇆ 🛎️

Brunkebergstorg 9 ✉ 111 51 – PLAN: B2
Ⓜ Kungsträdgården
TEL. 08-517 263 00 – **www**.scandichotels.com/downtowncamper
494 rm ⚏ – 🧍 1700/2300 SEK 🧍‍🧍 2150/3000 SEK – 20 suites

This unique hotel has an outside living theme: guest areas have urban-chic styling and eco-friendly bedrooms bring the outdoors indoors courtesy of window seats and natural materials. Creatively styled conference rooms come with games, each floor has a table tennis table and bikes, skateboards and kayaks are available for hire. The brasserie offers comforting fare.

ELITE EDEN PARK 🏚️

BUSINESS • CONTEMPORARY • MODERN

⛺ ♿ 🎐 🛌 AC 🚗

Sturegatan 22 ✉ 114 36 – PLAN: C1
Ⓜ Östermalmstorg
TEL. 08-555 627 00 – **www**.elite.se
124 rm ⚏ – 🧍 1300/3300 SEK 🧍‍🧍 1500/3500 SEK – 1 suite

A smart hotel in a converted office block, designed with the business traveller in mind. Stylish bedrooms boast comfy beds and large showers – some rooms overlook the park and some have small balconies. Choose from an Asian-inspired menu in Miss Voon or traditional British pub dishes in The Bishops Arms.

HAYMARKET BY SCANDIC

BUSINESS • HISTORIC BUILDING • ART DÉCO

Hötorget 13-15 ⊠ 111 57 – **PLAN: B2**
Ⓜ Hötorget
TEL. 08-517 267 00 – **www**.scandichotels.com/haymarket
401 rm ⌣ – ♦ 1600/2800 SEK ♦♦ 1700/3200 SEK – 7 suites

Built in the 1900s, this former department store sits overlooking the Square, just across from the Concert Hall. Swedish-born Greta Garbo once worked here and the décor, particularly in the bedrooms, gives a nod to the art deco style. There's a small movie theatre, a healthy café-cum-bistro, a European restaurant and an American bar which hosts jazz at weekends.

MISS CLARA BY NOBIS

BUSINESS • MODERN • PERSONALISED

Sveavägen 48 ⊠ 111 34 – **PLAN: B1**
Ⓜ Hötorget
TEL. 08-440 67 00 – **www**.missclarahotel.com
90 rm – ♦ 1590/2790 SEK ♦♦ 1690/3190 SEK, ⌣ 169 SEK – 2 suites

A fashionable hotel in a great location; it used to be a girls' school and its name is that of the former principal. Surprisingly quiet, dark wood bedrooms have good facilities. The atmospheric brasserie offers an international menu with an Italian slant and some classic Swedish specialities.

RADISSON BLU STRAND

BUSINESS • HISTORIC BUILDING • CONTEMPORARY

⇐ 佺 ఓ 祄 ⚎

Nybrokajen 9 box 16396 ⊠ 103 27 – PLAN: C2
Ⓜ Kungsträdgården
TEL. 08-506 640 00 – **www**.radissonblu.com/strandhotel-stockholm
160 rm – ♦ 1295/2695 SEK ♦♦ 1395/3395 SEK, ☲ 170 SEK – 11 suites

This imposing hotel part-dates from the 1912 Olympics and sits in a lively waterside spot overlooking Nybroviken. Bedrooms are a mix of traditional and modern styles; the Tower Suite boasts a roof terrace with stunning city views. Enjoy a mix of local and global dishes in the airy atrium restaurant.

ETT HEM

LUXURY • DESIGN • CLASSIC

⌕ 佺 祄 ⅃

Sköldungagatan 2 ⊠ 114 27 – PLAN: B1
Ⓜ Tekniska Högskolan
TEL. 08-20 05 90 – **www**.etthem.se
12 rm ☲ – ♦ 3920/4900 SEK ♦♦ 4720/5900 SEK

A charming Arts and Crafts townhouse built as a private residence in 1910. It's elegant, understated and makes good use of wood; its name means 'home' and that's exactly how it feels. Bedroom No.6 features an old chimney and No.1 has a four-poster and a huge marble bath. Modern set menus use top seasonal produce and are served in the kitchen, library and orangery.

LYDMAR

TOWNHOUSE • PERSONALISED • DESIGN

⟨ 斧 ᵹ AK

Södra Blasieholmshamnen 2 ✉ 111 48 – PLAN: C2
Ⓜ Kungsträdgården
TEL. 08-22 31 60 – **www**.lydmar.com
46 rm ⌫ – 👤 2700/3800 SEK 👥 3100/5200 SEK – 6 suites

Superbly located across the water from the Palace is this charming townhouse; formerly the store for the neighbouring museum's archives. It has a relaxed yet funky vibe and regularly changing contemporary artwork – and the roof terrace with its water feature is a delightful spot come summer. The attractive restaurant offers a modern European brasserie menu.

ELITE H. STOCKHOLM PLAZA

BUSINESS • CHAIN • CONTEMPORARY

斧 ᵹ 🛋 🏋

Birger Jarlsgatan 29 ✉ 103 95 – PLAN: B1
Ⓜ Östermalmstorg
TEL. 08-566 220 00 – **www**.elite.se
143 rm ⌫ – 👤 1290/2890 SEK 👥 1690/3290 SEK – 12 suites
VASSA EGGEN – See restaurant listing

The smaller sister of the Elite Eden Park is this attractive, centrally located building with a façade dating from 1884. Bright fabrics stand out against neutral walls in the compact modern bedrooms; go for one of the corner suites.

HOBO

BOUTIQUE HOTEL • UNIQUE • DESIGN

Brunkebergstorg 4 ⊠ 111 51 – PLAN: B2
Ⓜ Kungsträdgården
TEL. 08-578 827 00 – **www**.hobo.se
201 rm – ♠ 900/1700 SEK ♠♠ 1900/2200 SEK, ⊊ 120 SEK

With eco-inspired décor and quirky design features, Hobo offers
something a little different. The ground floor exhibits local businesses'
work and houses a laid-back bar-lounge serving modern menus.
Cleverly designed bedrooms come with headboards that transform
into desks and peg board walls hung with gadgets.

KUNGSTRÄDGÅRDEN

TOWNHOUSE • HISTORIC • PERSONALISED

Västra Trädgårdsgatan 11B ⊠ 11153 – PLAN: B2
Ⓜ Kungsträdgården
TEL. 08-440 66 50 – **www**.hotelkungstradgarden.se
94 rm ⊊ – ♠ 1450/2950 SEK ♠♠ 1750/3250 SEK

Overlooking the park of the same name is this part-18C building with
a classical façade and attractive original features. Bedrooms are
individually furnished in a Gustavian-style – it's worth paying the
extra for a bigger room. A concise menu of French-inspired dishes is
served in the covered courtyard.

RIDDARGATAN

BUSINESS • MODERN • PERSONALISED

🛅

Riddargatan 14 ✉ 114 35 – PLAN: C2
Ⓜ Östermalmstorg
TEL. 08-55573000 – **www**.ligula.se
78 rm 🛏 – ♦ 995/2995 SEK ♦♦ 1195/3195 SEK – 4 suites

This smart former office block is situated close to the shops and restaurants, and feels very much like a home-from-home. The newer bedrooms have bold designs and modern wet rooms. The contemporary breakfast room doubles as a lively bar.

TIME

BUSINESS • MODERN • PERSONALISED

♿ 🛎 🛅 🚗

Vanadisvägen 12 ✉ 113 46 – PLAN: A1
Ⓜ Odenplan
TEL. 08-54547300 – **www**.timehotel.se
144 rm 🛏 – ♦ 1850/2150 SEK ♦♦ 2050/2550 SEK

This purpose-built business hotel sits in a smart residential area on the edge of town and is run by a friendly, hands-on team. Bedrooms are bright, airy and of a good size; Superiors have Juliet balconies and Studios offer long-term lets.

CLARION COLLECTION H. WELLINGTON

BUSINESS • TOWNHOUSE • TRADITIONAL

Storgatan 6 ✉ 114 51 - **PLAN: C1**
Ⓜ Östermalmstorg
TEL. 08-667 09 10 - **www**.wellington.se
Closed 22 December-4 January
61 rm - 820/2420 SEK 1420/3220 SEK - 1 suite

Set in a former office block, this centrally located hotel makes an ideal base for shopping and sightseeing. Simple bedrooms feature bright fabrics and those on the top floor have city views. Buffet dinners are included in the price.

KAGGES 🕸

SWEDISH • FASHIONABLE • COSY

✗

Lilla Nygatan 21 ✉ 111 28 – **PLAN: F1**
Ⓜ Gamla Stan
– **www**.kagges.com
Closed January, midsummer and Monday-Tuesday
Menu 495 SEK – Carte 420/505 SEK (dinner only) (booking essential)

Two enthusiastic friends run this cosy restaurant with a lively buzz. Ask for a seat at the counter to watch the team prepare constantly evolving seasonal small plates with plenty of colour and a Swedish heart. 4 plates per person is about right or go for the 4 course Chef's Choice of the Day menu.

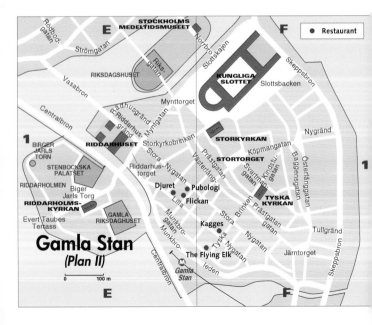

DJURET ﷽O

MEATS AND GRILLS • RUSTIC • NEIGHBOURHOOD XxX 🕸

Lilla Nygatan 5 ⊠ 111 28 – **PLAN: E1**
Ⓜ Gamla Stan
TEL. 08-506 400 84 – **www**.djuret.se
Closed July, Christmas and Sunday
Menu 595 SEK (dinner only) (tasting menu only) (booking essential)

Various rooms make up this atmospheric restaurant, including one part-built into the city walls and looking into the impressive wine cellar. Monthly set menus are formed around 3 key ingredients; masculine cooking has big, bold flavours.

FLICKAN ﷽O

MODERN CUISINE • FASHIONABLE • INTIMATE X 🄰🄲

Yxsmedsgränd 12 ⊠ 111 28 – **PLAN: E1**
Ⓜ Gamla Stan
TEL. 08-506 400 80 – **www**.restaurangflickan.se
Closed July, Christmas and Sunday-Wednesday
Menu 850 SEK (dinner only) (tasting menu only) (booking essential)

Pass through the busy bar to this small 16-seater restaurant, where you'll be greeted by a welcoming team. The 13 course set menu keeps Swedish produce to the fore, and modern dishes have the occasional Asian or South American twist.

THE FLYING ELK ⁄○

MODERN CUISINE • INN • FRIENDLY   ⅄

Mälartorget 15 ⊠ 111 27 – **PLAN: F1**
Ⓜ Gamla Stan
TEL. 08-20 85 83 – **www**.theflyingelk.se
Closed 24-25, 31 December, 1 January and midsummer
Carte 475/750 SEK (dinner only and lunch Saturday and Sunday)

A good night out is guaranteed at this lively corner spot, which is modelled on a British pub and has several different bars. Choose from bar snacks, pub dishes with a twist or a popular tasting menu of refined modern classics.

PUBOLOGI ⁄○

SWEDISH • COSY • NEIGHBOURHOOD   ⅩⅩ 🕸

Stora Nygatan 20 ⊠ 111 27 – **PLAN: E1**
Ⓜ Gamla Stan
TEL. 08-506 400 86 – **www**.pubologi.se
Closed July, Christmas, Sunday and Monday
Menu 650 SEK (dinner only) (tasting menu only) (booking advisable)

Book a window table at this charming modern bistro for views out over the cobbled street. The 5 course set menu offers refined, rustic dishes; flavours are strong and punchy and seasonality is key. The wine list is impressive.

OAXEN KROG ❀❀

CREATIVE • DESIGN • FRIENDLY ✕✕ ❀ ⟨ ⟨

Beckholmsvägen 26 (off Djurgårdsvägen) ✉ 115 21 – PLAN: D3
TEL. 08-55153105 – **www**.oaxen.com
Closed Christmas-New Year, Easter, midsummer, Sunday and
Monday
Menu 1900/2100 SEK (dinner only) (booking essential)

Chef:
Magnus Ek
Specialities:
Fermented and pickled vegetables
with ox marrow. Duck, forest
capers, fennel seeds and oak
moss. Rhubarb with celery sorbet
and fresh herbs.

This rebuilt boat shed sits in a delightful waterside location. Diners
are led through a door in Oaxen Slip into an oak-furnished room with
a slightly nautical feel. Beautifully constructed New Nordic dishes are
allied to nature and the seasons – they're delicate and balanced but
also offer depth of flavour.

OAXEN SLIP ☺

TRADITIONAL CUISINE • BISTRO ✕ ⟨ ⌂ ⌂

Beckholmsvägen 26 (off Djurgårdsvägen) ✉ 115 21 – PLAN: D3
TEL. 08-55153105 – **www**.oaxen.com
Closed Christmas
Carte 410/665 SEK

A bright, bustling bistro next to the old slipway; try for a spot on
the delightful terrace. Light floods the room and boats hang from
the girders in a nod to the local shipbuilding industry. The food is
wholesome and heartening and features plenty of seafood – whole
fish dishes are a speciality.

ULLA WINBLADH

SWEDISH • CLASSIC DÉCOR • COSY

Rosendalsvägen 8 ✉ 115 21 – **PLAN: D2**
TEL. 08-534 897 01 – **www**.ullawinbladh.se
Closed 24-25 December
Menu 595 SEK – Carte 440/660 SEK (booking essential)

Ulla Winbladh was originally built as a steam bakery for the 1897 Stockholm World Fair and is set in charming parkland beside the Skansen open-air museum. Sit on the terrace or in the older, more characterful part of the building. Hearty Swedish dishes include sweet and sour herring and fish roe.

POP HOUSE

BOUTIQUE HOTEL • PERSONALISED • MINIMALIST

Djurgårdsvägen 68 ✉ 115 21 – **PLAN: D2**
TEL. 08-502 541 40 – **www**.pophouse.se
49 rm ➘ – † 1195/3095 SEK †† 1295/3295 SEK – 2 suites

Pop House is ideally placed for visitors to the parks and museums of Djurgården. Bypass the queues waiting to enter 'ABBA The Museum', and head up to one of the spacious, simply furnished bedrooms; most have balconies with pleasant views. The small lounge, bar and restaurant are open-plan.

SKEPPSHOLMEN

HISTORIC · DESIGN · PERSONALISED

Gröna Gången 1 ⊠ 111 49 – PLAN: D2
TEL. 08-407 23 00 – **www**.hotelskeppsholmen.se
78 rm ⌂ – ♦ 1495/2995 SEK ♦♦ 1495/2995 SEK – 1 suite

This 17C hotel is perfect for a peaceful stay close to the city. It's set on a small island beside a beautiful park and was built by the king in 1699 for his soldiers (the conference room was once the officers' mess). White bedrooms have a minimalist style and sea or park views. Menus feature Swedish recipes.

BAR AGRIKULTUR ⊛

SWEDISH · COSY · NEIGHBOURHOOD

Skånegatan 79 (by Folkungagatan and Nytorgsgatan) ⊠ 116 35
Ⓜ Medborgarplatsen
– **www**.baragrikultur.se
Closed Christmas-New Year and midsummer
Carte 340/435 SEK (dinner only) (bookings not accepted)

The trendy Södermalm district is home to this intimate wine bar. The constantly changing blackboard menu lists fresh, tasty small plates which showcase the region's produce. The three stainless steel tanks contain home-distilled gin – flavours are changed regularly using various herbs, oils or fruits.

NOOK 🏠

MODERN CUISINE • INTIMATE • FRIENDLY   ✗

Åsögatan 176 ✉ 116 32 – PLAN: D3
Ⓜ Medborgarplatsen
TEL. 08-702 12 22 – **www**.nookrestaurang.se
Closed July, Christmas, Sunday and Monday
Menu 380/430 SEK (dinner only) (booking advisable)

This modern restaurant offers great value. Drop into the bar for Asian-influenced snacks or head to the intimately lit dining room with its checkerboard floor for one of two set menus. Creative cooking blends Swedish ingredients with Korean influences; order 3 days ahead for the suckling pig feast.

CAFÉ NIZZA 🍴

SWEDISH • BISTRO • NEIGHBOURHOOD   ✗ ⛱ A/C

Åsögatan 171 ✉ 116 32 – PLAN: D3
Ⓜ Medborgarplatsen
TEL. 08-640 99 50 – **www**.cafenizza.se
Closed 24-26 December, 1 January and midsummer
Menu 595 SEK (dinner only) (tasting menu only) (booking essential)

Drop in for a drink and some bar snacks or a 4 course set menu of unfussy, flavoursome dishes with a mix of Swedish and French influences. The small room has chequerboard flooring, a granite-topped bar and a bustling Parisian feel.

FOTOGRAFISKA 🍴

COUNTRY • RUSTIC • DESIGN   ✂✂ ⟨ ♿ A/C

Stadsgårdshamnen 22 ✉ 116 45 – **PLAN: D3**
Ⓜ Slussen
TEL. 08-509 00 500 – **www**.fotografiska.se
Closed July, 25 December, midsummer and Sunday
Menu 540 SEK – Carte 400/440 SEK (dinner only)

Take in lovely water views from the photography museum. From the room to the food, there's a green ethos, courtesy of reclaimed wood and ethical produce. Fresh, flavoursome dishes are largely vegetarian; go for 1 cold, 2 warm and 1 sweet.

HÄKTET 🍴

MODERN CUISINE • BISTRO • SIMPLE   ✗ 🏠 ⟷

Hornsgatan 82 ✉ 118 21 – **PLAN: B3**
Ⓜ Zinkensdamn
TEL. 08-845910 – **www**.haktet.se
Closed 24 and 31 December, 1 January, midsummer and Sunday
Carte 395/600 SEK (dinner only)

From 1781-1872 this was a debtors' prison. It has a characterful courtyard terrace and three bars – one in the style of a speakeasy, with a secret door. The simple bistro at the back serves classic Swedish dishes with a modern edge.

WOODSTOCKHOLM 🍴

MODERN CUISINE · BISTRO · NEIGHBOURHOOD ╳ 🏠 ☕

Mosebacke Torg 9 ✉ 116 46 – **PLAN: C3**
Ⓜ Slussen
TEL. 08-36 93 99 – **www**.woodstockholm.com
Closed Christmas, Sunday and Monday
Menu 565 SEK – Carte 525/620 SEK (dinner only and lunch Friday)

A chef-turned-furniture-maker owns this neighbourhood restaurant overlooking the park. Cooking follows a theme which changes every 2 months and dishes are simple yet full of flavour. In summer, the private room opens as a wine bar.

RIVAL 🏠

BOUTIQUE HOTEL · BUSINESS · PERSONALISED

⚐ ♿ 🍴

Mariatorget 3 ✉ 118 91 – **PLAN: B3**
Ⓜ Mariatorget
TEL. 08-545 789 00 – **www**.rival.se
99 rm ⌕ – 🛉 1195/2595 SEK 🛉🛉 1695/4195 SEK – 2 suites

The location is delightful: opposite a beautiful square with gardens and a fountain. It's owned by ABBA's Benny Andersson and the stylish bedrooms come with Swedish movie themes and murals of famous scenes; the 700-seater art deco theatre also hosts regular events and shows. Dine on global dishes either in the bistro or on the balcony; the café is popular for snacks.

CLARION H. ARLANDA AIRPORT

BUSINESS • MODERN • ECO-FRIENDLY

😋 🦽 🏋 🛎 ♨️ AC 🏊

Tornvägen 2, Sky City (at Terminals 4-5, 1st floor above street
level) ✉ 190 45
TEL. 08-444 18 00 – **www**.choice.se/clarion/arlandaairport.se
414 rm ⌣ – 🛏 990/2900 SEK 🛏🛏 1200/3100 SEK – 13 suites

A sleek, corporate hotel next to Terminals 4 and 5, with sound eco-
credentials – they even make honey from their own hives. Relax in
the large 'Living Room' lounge area or in the outside pool, then have
dinner in the bistro which offers a mix of international and Swedish
dishes along with runway views.

STALLMÄSTAREGÅRDEN

INN • HISTORIC BUILDING • COSY

🍺 😋 🏊 P

Nortull (North: 2 km by Sveavägen) ✉ 113 47
TEL. 08-610 13 00 – **www**.stallmastaregarden.se
Closed 23-30 December
49 rm ⌣ – 🛏 1995/3120 SEK 🛏🛏 1995/3120 SEK – 3 suites

You can enjoy beautiful views over the water to the Royal Park from
this brightly painted inn, which dates from the 17C. It comprises
several buildings set around a garden courtyard. Cosy bedrooms
have a classic style and Oriental touches. Modern Swedish cuisine is
influenced by classic Tore Wretman recipes.

VILLA KÄLLHAGEN

TRADITIONAL · BUSINESS · MINIMALIST

≤ 🦢 🛏 ✾ 🎐 AC 🛅 P

Djurgårdsbrunnsvägen 10 (East: 3 km by Strandvägen) ✉ 115 27
TEL. 08-665 03 00 – **www**.kallhagen.se
36 rm ⬡ – 🛉 1295/2795 SEK 🛉🛉 1495/2995 SEK – 3 suites

This well-run hotel is a popular place for functions, but with its tranquil waterside location, it's a hit with leisure guests too. Bedrooms feature four different colour schemes – inspired by the seasons – and have park or water views. The modern Swedish menu has a classic edge and comes with wine pairings.

FJÄDERHOLMARNAS KROG ⫶○

SEAFOOD · FRIENDLY · RUSTIC   XX ≤ ᕕ 🎐

Stora Fjäderholmen (East: 25 minutes by boat from berth
13 Nybrokajen) ✉ 111 15
TEL. 08-718 833 55 – **www**.fjaderholmarnaskrog.se
Closed 29 September-23 November and 22 December-26 April
Menu 330/545 SEK – Carte 415/715 SEK (booking essential)

The location is idyllic and on a sunny day nothing beats a spot on the terrace watching the ships glide through the archipelago. The airy interior has a boathouse feel. Classic seafood dishes are replaced by a buffet table at Christmas.

ALOË ✿

CREATIVE • RUSTIC • INTIMATE XX

Svartlösavägen 52 ✉ 125 33
TEL. 08-556 36168 – **www**.aloerestaurant.se
Closed Sunday-Tuesday

Menu 1600 SEK (dinner only) (surprise menu only) (booking essential)

Chef:
Niclas Jönsson and Daniel Höglander

Specialities:
Langoustine, fermented beans and gochujang. Aged pork loin, apple and vin jaune. "Forêt-Noire" with shiso

Unusually hidden in an old suburban supermarket, this warm, welcoming restaurant is run by two talented chefs. Snacks at the kitchen counter are followed by a locally-influenced surprise menu with a seafood bias. Creative dishes stimulate the senses with their intense flavours and original combinations.

LUX DAG FÖR DAG ❧

MODERN CUISINE • BRASSERIE •
NEIGHBOURHOOD XX ⪕ 🕭 🏠 🅰🅲

Primusgatan 116 (West: 5.5 km by Norr Mälarstrand) ✉ 112 67
TEL. 08-619 0190 – **www**.luxdagfordag.se
Closed 23 December-7 January, 16 July-16 August, Saturday lunch, Sunday and Monday

Menu 580 SEK (dinner) – Carte 325/725 SEK

A bright, modern, brasserie-style restaurant in an old waterside Electrolux factory dating back to 1916. Generously proportioned dishes might look modern but they have a traditional base; sourcing Swedish ingredients is paramount.

BOCKHOLMEN ¶O

SWEDISH • TRADITIONAL DÉCOR •
COUNTRY HOUSE   XX ⋖ 🏠 ⇔ P

Bockholmsvägen (Northwest: 7 km by Sveavägen and E18) ✉ 170 78
Ⓜ Bergshamra
TEL. 08-624 22 00 – **www**.bockholmen.com
Closed 22 December-10 January, midsummer, lunch October-April
and Monday
Carte 425/625 SEK (booking essential)

With charming terraces leading down to the water, and an outside bar,
this 19C summer house is the perfect place to relax on a summer's day.
It's set on a tiny island, so opening times vary. Wide-ranging menus
include weekend brunch.

ULRIKSDALS WÄRDSHUS ¶O

TRADITIONAL CUISINE • INN •
ROMANTIC   XX ⋖ 🛏 ⇔ P

Ulriksdals Slottspark (Northwest: 8 km by Sveavägen and E 18 towards
Norrtälje then take first junction for Ulriksdals Slott) ✉ 170 79
Ⓜ Bergshamra
TEL. 08-85 08 15 – **www**.ulriksdalswardshus.se
Closed Sunday dinner
Menu 470 SEK (weekday lunch)/945 SEK – Carte 475/830 SEK
(booking essential)

A charming 19C wood-built inn located on the edge of a woodland;
start with drinks on the terrace overlooking the lake. Every table in the
New England style room has an outlook over the attractive gardens
and there's a characterful wine cellar. Classic Swedish dishes are
supplemented by a smörgåsbord at lunch.

GOTHENBURG

Sweden

Gothenburg is considered to be one of Sweden's friendliest towns, a throwback to its days as a leading trading centre. This is a compact, pretty city whose roots go back four hundred years. It has trams, broad avenues and canals and its centre is boisterous but never feels tourist heavy or overcrowded. Gothenburgers take life at a more leisurely pace than their Stockholm cousins over on the east coast. The mighty shipyards that once dominated the shoreline are now quiet; go to the centre, though, and you find the good-time

ambience of Avenyn, a vivacious thoroughfare full of places in which to shop, eat and drink. But for those still itching for a feel of the heavy industry that once defined the place, there's a Volvo museum sparkling with chrome and shiny steel. The Old Town is the historic heart of the city: its tight grid of streets has grand façades and a fascinating waterfront. Just west is the Vasastan quarter, full of fine National Romantic buildings. Further west again is Haga, an old working-class district which has been gentrified, its cobbled streets sprawling with trendy cafes and boutiques. Adjacent to Haga is the district of Linné, a vibrant area with its elegantly tall 19th century Dutch-inspired buildings. As this is a maritime town, down along the quayside is as good a place to get your bearings as any.

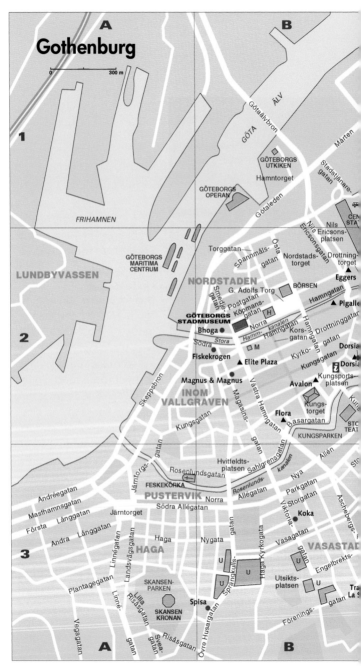

Gothenburg

0   300 m

A

B

1

GÖTA ÄLV

Götaälvbron

GÖTA

Mårten

Stadstjänare-gatan

GÖTEBORGS
UTKIKEN

Hamntorget

GÖTEBORGS
OPERAN

Götaleden

CEN
STA

Nils
Ericsons-
platsen

Drottning-
torget

FRIHAMNEN

Nils Ericssonsgatan

Östra
Spannmåls-
gatan

Torggatan

Nordstads-
torget

GÖTEBORGS
MARITIMA
CENTRUM

LUNDBYVASSEN

2

NORDSTADEN

Eggers

BÖRSEN

Pigalle

Smedje-
gatan

G. Adolfs Torg

Hamngatan

Postgatan

Köpmans-
gatan

GÖTEBORGS
STADSMUSEUM

H

Drottninggatan

Bhoga

Norra
Hamn-
Hamngatan
kanalen

Drottninggatan

Hamngatan

Stora

Kors-
gatan

Dorsia

Södra

M

Kyrko-
gatan

Dorsia

Fiskekrogen

Elite Plaza

Kungsgatan

Kungsports-
platsen

Magnus & Magnus

Avalon

Västra Hamngatan

INOM
VALLGRAVEN

Magasins-
gatan

Flora

Kungs-
torget

STC
TEAT

Skeppsbron

Vasargatan

Kullе

Kungsgatan

KUNGSPARKEN

Allén

3

Hvitfeldts-
platsen

Sahlgrensgatan

Nya

Sto

Rosenlundsgatan

kanalen

FESKEKÖRKA

Rosenlunds-

PUSTERVIK

Norra

Allégatan

Parkgatan

Andréegatan

Jämtorgs-
gatan

Södra Allégatan

Storgatan

Koka

Masthamnsgatan

Järntorget

Nya
Viktoria-

VASASTAD

Första
Långgatan

Linnégatan

Haga

Vasagatan

Andra Långgatan

Landsvägsgatan

Nygata

Haga Kyrkogata

Engelbrekts-

Plantagegatan

Linné-

Lilla Risåsgatan

SKANSEN-
PARKEN

Sprängkullsgatan

U

U

Utsikts-
platsen

U

Tra
La S

Vegagatan

Linné-
gatan

SKANSEN
KRONAN

Spisa

Övre Husargatan

Risåsgatan

Svea-
gatan

Förenings-
gatan

Ascheberg-
gatan

Vasagatan

A

B

216

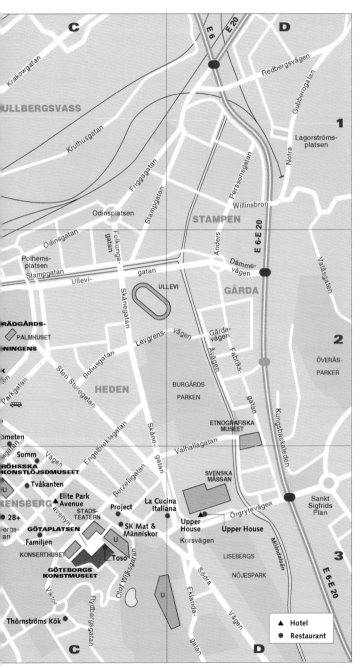

BHOGA 🕸

CREATIVE • DESIGN • FASHIONABLE   ✗

Norra Hamngatan 10 ✉ 411 14 – PLAN: B2
TEL. 031-13 80 18 – **www**.bhoga.se
Closed 1 week Christmas, 1 week August, Sunday and Monday
Menu 600/900 SEK (dinner only) (tasting menu only)

Chef:
Gustav Knutsson

Specialities:
Mackerel with green strawberries and blackcurrant leaves. Smoked turbot, turnips and gooseberries. Beach Rose sorbet, red berries and cream.

A chic, contemporary restaurant with an elegant feel, which is passionately run by two well-travelled friends and their charmingly attentive team. Top quality seasonal ingredients are used in imaginative ways, creating provocative yet harmonious texture and flavour combinations. Wine pairings are original.

KOKA 🕸

MODERN CUISINE • DESIGN • NEIGHBOURHOOD   ✗ A/C

Viktoriagatan 12 ✉ 411 25 – PLAN: B3
TEL. 031-701 79 79 – **www**.restaurangkoka.se
Closed July, Christmas and Sunday
Menu 480/880 SEK (dinner only) (tasting menu only)

Specialities:
Mackerel, rhubarb and beetroot. Lamb, marigold and shellfish salt. Strawberries with marjoram and mustard.

An understatedly elegant room with wooden planks on the floors and walls and wooden furniture to match. Choose 3, 5 or 7 courses from the daily set menu; dishes are light and refreshingly playful in their approach and fish features highly. Well-chosen wines and smooth service complete the picture.

SK MAT & MÄNNISKOR ✿

MODERN CUISINE • DESIGN • NEIGHBOURHOOD 🍴🍴   ♿   A/C

Johannebergsgatan 24 ✉ 412 55 – PLAN: C3
TEL. 031-812580 – **www**.skmat.se
Closed 5 weeks summer, Christmas, Sunday and bank holidays
Menu 595 SEK – Carte 535/560 SEK (dinner only) (booking essential)

Chef:
Stefan Karlsson

Specialities:
Chanterelles with egg custard. Lamb, carrots, wild pepper, spring onion and lamb jus. Strawberries with violet ice cream and strawberry curd.

The main focal point of this buzzy restaurant is the 360° open kitchen; not only can you watch the chefs at work but they also deliver your food. The effort put into sourcing and the reverence with which ingredients are treated is commendable and dishes are exciting and packed with flavour.

THÖRNSTRÖMS KÖK ✿

CLASSIC CUISINE • NEIGHBOURHOOD • ROMANTIC   🍴🍴🍴   🍷   A/C   ✷

Teknologgatan 3 ✉ 411 32 – PLAN: C3
TEL. 031-16 20 66 – **www**.thornstromskok.com
Closed 7 July-14 August, 22 December-3 January, Easter and Sunday
Menu 675 SEK – Carte 695/755 SEK (dinner only) (booking essential)

Chef:
Håkan Thörnström

Specialities:
Sweetbreads, salsify and morels. Poached turbot with burnt broccoli. Variations of blackberry, roasted wheat, lovage and rapeseed oil.

An elegant, long-standing restaurant with a stunning wine cave; set in a quiet residential area and run by a welcoming, knowledgeable team. There's a good choice of menus, including 4 different tasting options. Precise, confident, classically based cooking uses top quality produce to create pronounced flavours.

28+ ✿

MODERN CUISINE • ROMANTIC • INTIMATE   XX 🍴 A/C ⟷

Götabergsgatan 28 ✉ 411 34 – PLAN: C3
TEL. 031-20 21 61 – **www**.28plus.se
Closed 1 July-21 August, Christmas, New Year, Sunday, Monday and
bank holidays
Menu 895 SEK – Carte 595/675 SEK (dinner only)

Specialities:
Scallop, bacon, peas
and caviar. Lemon sole with
ramsons and asparagus beurre
blanc. Blueberry sorbet with
whipped cream cheese.

This passionately run basement restaurant has been a Gothenburg
institution for over 30 years. Modern cooking showcases prime
seasonal ingredients, skilfully blending French and Swedish influences
to create intricate, flavourful dishes. There's an exceptional cheese
selection and an outstanding wine list.

UPPER HOUSE ✿

CREATIVE • ELEGANT • CHIC   XXX 🍴 ≤ & A/C

Upper House Hotel • Gothia Towers (25th Floor), Mässans gata
24 ✉ 402 26 – PLAN: D3
TEL. 031-708 82 00 – **www**.upperhouse.se
Closed 10 July-7 August, 23-25 December, Sunday and Monday
Menu 995/1400 SEK (dinner only) (tasting menu only) (booking
essential)

Specialities:
Quail egg, lemon and dried
bleak roe. Courgette flower
with sweetbreads and tomato.
Cinnamon madeleine with apple
butter.

Look out from the 25th floor over 360° of twinkling city lights. Start
with snacks in the plush bar then watch your bread being cooked
over a hot stone. Two set menus offers elaborate, visually pleasing,
flavourful dishes made with an abundance of local ingredients.
Service is attentive and professional.

FAMILJEN 🍴

SCANDINAVIAN • DESIGN • NEIGHBOURHOOD   🍴 🐝 🪑 AC

Arkivgatan 7 ✉ 411 34 – PLAN: C3
TEL. 031-20 79 79 – **www**.restaurangfamiljen.se
Closed Christmas and Sunday

Menu 375/475 SEK – Carte 340/500 SEK (dinner only) (booking essential)

A lively, friendly eatery divided into three parts: a bar with bench seating and an open kitchen; a bright red room with a characterful cellar and a glass wine cave; and a superb wrap-around terrace. Cooking is good value and portions are generous. There's an appealing wine, beer and cocktail list too.

PROJECT 🍴

MODERN CUISINE • NEIGHBOURHOOD •
FASHIONABLE   🍴 🪑 🏮

Södra vägen 45 ✉ 412 54 – PLAN: C3
TEL. 031-18 18 58 – **www**.projectgbg.com
Closed Christmas and Sunday-Tuesday

Menu 525/725 SEK – Carte 450/535 SEK (dinner only) (booking essential)

A young couple and their charming service team run this cosy little bistro. Creative dishes are Swedish at heart and full of flavour; the delicious bread takes 5 days to make and the homemade butter, 2 days. Flexible menus allow diners to tailor their experience and provide the opportunity for sharing.

SOMM 🍎

MODERN CUISINE · RUSTIC · COSY

Lorensbergsgatan 8 ✉ 411 36 – PLAN: C3
TEL. 031-28 28 40 – www.somm.se
Closed July, Christmas and midsummer

Menu 425 SEK – Carte 520/625 SEK (dinner only)

A simply but warmly decorated neighbourhood bistro with contemporary artwork and a cosy, friendly feel. Quality seasonal ingredients are used to create tasty modern dishes, which feature on an à la carte and various tasting menus. The wine list offers great choice and the service is charming and professional.

LA CUCINA ITALIANA 🍴

ITALIAN · INTIMATE · NEIGHBOURHOOD

Skånegatan 33 ✉ 412 52 – PLAN: C/D3
TEL. 031-16 63 07 – www.lacucinaitaliana.nu
Closed 2 weeks July, Christmas, Easter, midsummer and Sunday

Menu 400/700 SEK – Carte 430/620 SEK (dinner only) (booking essential)

An enthusiastically run restaurant consisting of 6 tables. Choose between the à la carte, a daily fixed price menu and a 6 course surprise tasting 'journey'. The chef-owner regularly travels to Italy to buy cheeses, meats and wines.

DORSIA ⅋○

MODERN CUISINE • EXOTIC DÉCOR •
ROMANTIC   XX ⅋ 🏠 AC ⟳

Dorsia Hotel • Trädgårdsgatan 6 ✉ 411 08 – **PLAN: B2**
TEL. 031-790 10 00 – **www**.dorsia.se
Menu 385 SEK – Carte 600/800 SEK

 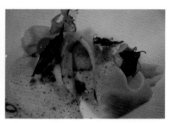

A dramatic hotel dining room split over two levels, with striking
flower arrangements, gloriously quirky lighting, and belle époque
oil paintings hanging proudly on the walls. Local fish features highly
and puddings are worth saving room for. The impressive wine list is
rich in burgundies and clarets.

FISKEKROGEN ⅋○

SEAFOOD • ELEGANT • CLASSIC DÉCOR   XX ⅋ AC ⟳

Lilla Torget 1 ✉ 411 18 – **PLAN: B2**
TEL. 031-10 10 05 – **www**.fiskekrogen.se
Closed mid July-mid August, Christmas, New Year, Easter and
Sunday
Menu 495 SEK – Carte 525/800 SEK (dinner only and Saturday
lunch)

This charming restaurant is set within a 1920s columned Grand Café
and showcases top quality seafood in classical dishes; the seafood
buffet on Friday and Saturday is impressive. 'Bifångst' offers a tasting
menu of modern small plates.

KOMETEN ⅼO

SWEDISH • TRADITIONAL DÉCOR • NEIGHBOURHOOD XX 🏠

Vasagatan 58 ✉ 411 37 – PLAN: C2
TEL. 031-13 79 88 – **www**.restaurangkometen.se
Closed 23-27 December, 1 January and midsummer

Carte 335/790 SEK (booking essential)

The oldest restaurant in town has a classic façade and a homely,
traditional feel; it opened in 1934 and is now part-owned by celebrated
chef Leif Mannerström. Sweden's culinary traditions are kept alive
here in generous, tasty dishes.

MAGNUS & MAGNUS ⅼO

MODERN CUISINE • FASHIONABLE •
NEIGHBOURHOOD ⅼ 🏠

Magasinsgatan 8 ✉ 411 18 – PLAN: B2
TEL. 031-13 30 00 – **www**.magnusmagnus.se
Closed 24-25 December, Sunday and Monday

Menu 495/745 SEK – Carte 440/555 SEK (dinner only)

A trendy restaurant with a warm, intimate atmosphere, a central bar,
an open kitchen and a bright, well-informed team. Modern Nordic
cooking has the occasional Asian twist; most diners plump for the
set 4 course menu.

SJÖMAGASINET ⅃O

SWEDISH • RUSTIC • TRADITIONAL
DÉCOR

Adolf Edelsvärds gata 5, Klippans Kulturreservat 5 (Southwest:
3.5 km by Andréeg taking Kiel-Klippan exit (Stena Line), or boat
from Rosenlund. Also evenings and weekends in summer from Lilla
Bommens Hamn) ✉ 414 51
TEL. 031-775 59 20 – **www**.sjomagasinet.se
Closed 23 December-10 January, Saturday lunch and Sunday
Menu 595/925 SEK – Carte 745/1165 SEK

A charming split-level restaurant in an old East India Company
warehouse dating from 1775; ask for a table on the upper floor to take
in the lovely harbour view. Cooking offers a pleasing mix of classic
and modern dishes; lunch sees a concise version of the à la carte and
a 3 course set menu.

SPISA ⅃O

MEDITERRANEAN CUISINE • FASHIONABLE •
NEIGHBOURHOOD

Övre Husargatan 3 ✉ 411 22 – **PLAN: B3**
TEL. 031-386 06 10 – **www**.spisamatbar.se
Closed dinner Monday and lunch Saturday and Sunday
Menu 295/495 SEK – Carte 305/445 SEK

A contemporary restaurant set in an up-and-coming area a short
walk from the city centre and frequented by a lively, sociable crowd.
The menu offers tasty sharing plates with French, Spanish and Italian
origins. Try a cocktail too.

TOSO ⫶○

ASIAN • BISTRO • EXOTIC DÉCOR   ✗ Ⓐ/C

Götaplatsen ⊠ 412 56 – PLAN: C3
TEL. 031-787 98 00 – **www**.toso.nu
Closed Christmas, 1 January and bank holidays

Carte 355/550 SEK (dinner only)

There's something for everyone at this modern Asian restaurant,
where terracotta warriors stand guard and loud music pumps through
the air. Dishes mix Chinese and Japanese influences; start with some
of the tempting small plates.

TRATTORIA LA STREGA ⫶○

ITALIAN • FRIENDLY • BISTRO   ✗ 🏠

Aschebergsgatan 23B ⊠ 411 27 – PLAN: B3
TEL. 031-18 15 01 – **www**.trattorialastrega.se
Closed July, 24 December-6 January and Monday

Menu 600 SEK – Carte 320/530 SEK (dinner only) (booking
essential)

 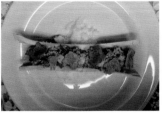

A lively little trattoria in a quiet residential area; run by a charming
owner. Sit at a candlelit table to enjoy authentic, boldly flavoured
Italian cooking and well-chosen wines. Signature dishes include pasta
with King crab ragout.

TVÅKANTEN ⭐🍴

TRADITIONAL CUISINE • BRASSERIE • NEIGHBOURHOOD

Kungsportsavenyn 27 ✉ 411 36 – **PLAN: C3**
TEL. 031-18 21 15 – **www**.tvakanten.se
Closed Christmas, Easter, midsummer and bank holidays
Menu 645 SEK (dinner) – Carte 395/705 SEK

With its welcoming hum and friendly team, it's no wonder this long-standing family-run restaurant is always busy. The dimly-lit, brick-walled dining room is the place to eat. Homely lunches are followed by more ambitious dinners.

VRÅ 🍴

JAPANESE • FASHIONABLE • SIMPLE

Clarion Hotel Post, Drottningtorget 10 ✉ 411 03 – **PLAN: C2**
TEL. 031-619060 – **www**.restaurangvra.se
Closed 12 July-12 August, Christmas, Sunday and Monday
Menu 495/1050 SEK – Carte 335/545 SEK (dinner only)

A modern hotel restaurant run by an attentive, knowledgeable team. Their tagline is 'Swedish ingredients, Japanese flavours' and the produce is top quality. Choose the 8 course set menu or a menu with 3 core dishes which you can add to.

ELITE PARK AVENUE

BUSINESS • TRADITIONAL • MODERN

← 穴 ⋔ ⅃♨ AC ⅃♨ 🚗

Kungsportsavenyn 36-38 ✉ 400 15 – PLAN: C3
TEL. 031-727 10 76 – **www**.parkavenuecafe.se
317 rm ☕ – ♦ 1050/2350 SEK ♦♦ 1250/2750 SEK – 9 suites

Set in a lively location close to many museums and galleries, the
Elite Park Avenue is a popular place for conferences. The interior
is stylish and the bedrooms are spacious and well-equipped – the
rooftop suites come with balconies. Dine in the English pub or on
French or Swedish dishes in the bistro.

ELITE PLAZA

TRADITIONAL • BUSINESS • MODERN

穴 ⋔ ⅃♨ ⅃♨ 🚗

Västra Hamngatan 3 ✉ 402 22 – PLAN: B2
TEL. 031-720 40 40 – **www**.elite.se
Closed 22-26 December
127 rm ☕ – ♦ 1200/2900 SEK ♦♦ 1400/3900 SEK – 3 suites

This elegant building dates back to the 19C and features ornate
ceilings and a Venetian-style sitting room. Bedrooms seamlessly
blend the classic and the modern and the service is welcoming and
personalised. The restaurant sits within a glass-enclosed courtyard
and mixes French and Scandinavian influences.

UPPER HOUSE

LUXURY • BUSINESS • MODERN

Gothia Towers, Mässans gata 24 ⊠ 402 26 – **PLAN: D3**
TEL. 031-708 82 00 – **www**.upperhouse.se
53 rm ⌛ – ♦ 2890/5390 SEK ♦♦ 2890/5390 SEK – 1 suite
UPPER HOUSE ❀ – See restaurant listing

Set at the top of one of the Gothia Towers; take in the dramatic
view from the terrace or from the lovely three-storey spa. Spacious
bedrooms are filled with top electronic equipment and Scandic art
– the duplex suites are sublime.

AVALON

BUSINESS • BOUTIQUE HOTEL • DESIGN

Kungstorget 9 ⊠ 411 17 – **PLAN: B2**
TEL. 031-751 02 00 – **www**.avalonhotel.se
101 rm ⌛ – ♦ 1245/2445 SEK ♦♦ 1445/2745 SEK – 3 suites

A boutique hotel in a great location near the shops, theatres and river.
Designer bedrooms have the latest mod cons and come with stylish
bathrooms; the penthouse suites have balconies. Relax in the rooftop
pool then head for the all-day bistro, which opens onto the piazza and
serves international cuisine.

CENTRE

DORSIA

🏠

TOWNHOUSE • LUXURY • ART DÉCO

⚐ A/C 🛋

Trädgårdsgatan 8 ✉ 411 08 – PLAN: B2
TEL. 031-790 10 00 – **www**.dorsia.se
37 rm ⌑ – 🛉 2000 SEK 🛉🛉 2600/7000 SEK
DORSIA – See restaurant listing

Exuberant, eccentric, seductive and possibly a little decadent, this
townhouse hotel comes with a theatrical belle époque style, where
art from the owner's personal collection, fine fabrics and rich colours
add to the joie de vivre. The restaurant is equally vibrant and the
atmosphere suitably relaxed. The Salon is set to serve gourmet
dinners as of Spring 2018.

EGGERS

🏠

TRADITIONAL • LUXURY • ELEGANT

⚐ 🛋

Drottningtorget 2-4 ✉ 411 03 – PLAN: B2
TEL. 031-333 44 40 – **www**.hoteleggers.se
Closed 22-27 December
69 rm ⌑ – 🛉 995/2190 SEK 🛉🛉 1220/3325 SEK

An elegant railway hotel that opened in 1859 with electricity and a
telephone in every room. The warm, welcoming interior features old
wrought iron, stained glass and period furnishings. The characterful
restaurant still has its original wallpaper and offers Swedish and
French favourites.

Dejan Sokolovski/Dorsia • Dejan Sokolovski/Dorsia • Hotel Eggers • Hotel Eggers

PIGALLE

TOWNHOUSE • FAMILY • VINTAGE

Södra Hamngatan 2A ✉ 411 06 – **PLAN: B2**
TEL. 031-80 29 21 – **www**.hotelpigalle.se
60 rm ☕ – ♦ 1000/1700 SEK ♦♦ 1700/2600 SEK – 1 suite

A top-hatted manager will welcome you to the reception-cum-welcome-bar of this quirky hotel, which is set within the walls of a historic building. The décor is bold and eclectic, with dramatic features and plenty of personality. In the restaurant you can choose to sit at proper tables or on comfy sofas.

FLORA

FAMILY • BUSINESS • DESIGN

Grönsakstorget 2 ✉ 411 17 – **PLAN: B2**

TEL. 031-13 86 16 – **www**.hotelflora.se
Closed 22 December- 2 January
70 rm ☕ – ♦ 1120/1720 SEK ♦♦ 1450/1970 SEK

This well-located Victorian mid-terrace is nicely run and has a relaxed, funky feel. Bedrooms benefit from high ceilings; ask for one of the newer, designer rooms. The bar-lounge is a popular spot and doubles as the breakfast room.

VILLAN

TRADITIONAL • FAMILY • COSY

Sjöportsgatan 2 (West: 6 km by Götaälvbron and Lundbyleden, or boat from Rosenlund) ✉ 417 64
TEL. 031-725 77 77 – **www**.hotelvillan.com
26 rm ☲ – ♦ 1100/1600 SEK ♦♦ 1300/2000 SEK

A characterful wood-clad, family-run house; once home to a shipbuilding manager and later floated over to this location. The stylish interior has smart, clean lines. Contemporary bedrooms boast good mod cons – No. 31 has a sauna and a TV in the bathroom. The first floor restaurant overlooks the river.

LANDVETTER AIRPORT HOTEL

BUSINESS • FAMILY • DESIGN

Flygets Hotellväg (East: 30 km by Rd 40) ✉ 438 13
TEL. 031-97 75 50 – **www**.landvetterairporthotel.com
187 rm ☲ – ♦ 1595 SEK ♦♦ 1695/2495 SEK – 1 suite

A family-run hotel located just minutes from the airport terminal. The light, open interior has a calm air and a fresh Scandic style, and bedrooms have an unfussy retro feel. The informal restaurant offers a mix of Swedish and global dishes, along with a BBQ and grill menu at dinner.

MALMÖ

Sweden

Malmö was founded in the 13C under Danish rule and it wasn't until 1658 that it entered Swedish possession and subsequently established itself as one of the world's biggest shipyards. The building of the 8km long Oresund Bridge in 2000 reconnected the city with Denmark and a year later, the Turning Torso apartment block was built in the old shipyard district, opening up the city to the waterfront. Once an industrial hub, this 'city of knowledge' has impressively green credentials: buses run on natural gas and there are

400km of bike lanes. There's plenty of green space too; you can picnic in Kungsparken or Slottsparken, sit by the lakes in Pildammsparken or pet the farm animals in 'Folkets'. At the heart of this vibrant city lie three squares: Gustav Adolfs Torg, Stortorget and Lilla Torg, connected by a pedestrianised shopping street. You'll find some of Malmö's oldest buildings in Lilla Torg, along with bustling open-air brasseries; to the west is Scandinavia's oldest surviving Renaissance castle and its beautiful gardens – and beyond that, the 2km Ribersborg Beach with its open-air baths. North is Gamla Väster with its charming houses and galleries, while south is Davidshall, filled with designer boutiques and chic eateries. Further south is Möllevångstorget, home to a throng of reasonably priced Asian and Middle Eastern shops.

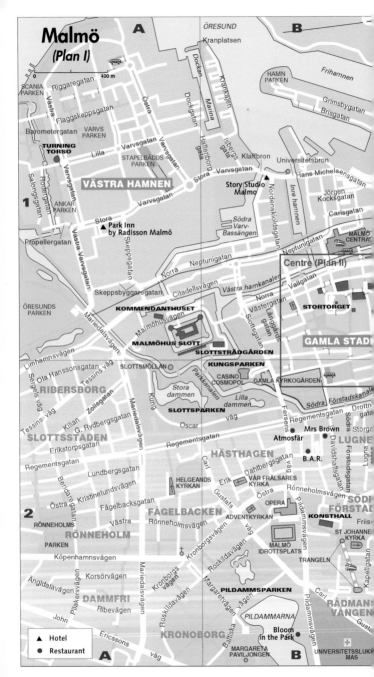

Malmö
(Plan I)

0   400 m

ÖRESUND

Kranplatsen

A

B

SCANIA PARKEN

Riggaregatan

HAMN PARKEN

Frihamnen

Grimsbygatan

Brisgatan

Flaggskeppsgatan

Barometergatan

VARVS PARKEN

Östra

Dockan

Krankajen

Marina

TURNING TORSO

Lilla

Varvsgatan

Varvsgatan

STAPELBÄDDS PARKEN

Hallenborgs gata

Isbergs gata

Klaffbron

Universitetsbron

Hans Michelsensgatan

Saborgsgatan

Rodergatan

VÄSTRA HAMNEN

Stora Varvsgatan

Story Studio Malmö

Nordenskiöldsgatan

Inre hamnen

Jörgen Kocksgatan

Carlsgatan

1

ANKAR PARKEN

Varvsgatan

▲ Stora
Park Inn
by Radisson Malmö

Södra Varv-Bassängen

MALMÖ CENTRAL

Propellergatan

Västra Varvsgatan

Skeppsgatan

Neptunigatan

Neptunigatan

Centre (Plan II)

Norra

ÖRESUNDS PARKEN

Skeppsbyggaregatan

Citadellsvägen

Västra hamkanalen

Vallgatan

Norra

STORTORGET

KOMMENDANTHUSET

Mariedalsvägen

Malmöhusvägen

Västergatan

Ängdsgatan

Slottsgatan

MALMÖHUS SLOTT

SLOTTSTRÄDGÅRDEN

GAMLA STAD

Limhamnsvägen

SLOTTSMÖLLAN

KUNGSPARKEN

Parkkanalen

CASINO COSMOPOL

GAMLA KYRKOGÅRDEN

Ola Hanssonsgatan

Tessins väg

Stora dammen

Fersens

Kung

Lilla dammen

SLOTTSPARKEN

Södra Förstadskanal

Sergels väg

Tessins väg

Kilian

Zollgatan

G. Rydbergsgatan

Oscar

väg

Regementsgatan

Södra

Drottn gata

Storga

RIBERSBORG

Mariedalsvägen

Mrs Brown

LUGNE

SLOTTSSTADEN

Erikstorpsgatan

Regementsgatan

Atmosfär ●

Davidshallsgatan

Förstadsgatan

Regementsgatan

Lundbergsgatan

Kristinelundsvägen

HÄSTHAGEN

Dahlbergsgatan

B.A.R.

Bergdalagatan

HELGEANDS KYRKAN

Erik

VÅR FRÄLSARES KYRKA

Östra

Rönneholmsvägen

SÖDR

Östra

Fågelbacksgatan

Gustafs

OPERA

Pildammsvägen

FÖRSTAD

2

FÅGELBACKEN

ADVENTKYRKAN

KONSTHALL

Friis-

RÖNNEHOLMS

Västra

Rönneholmsvägen

väg

MALMÖ IDROTTSPLATS

ST JOHANNE KYRKA

RÖNNEHOLM

PARKEN

Kronborgsvägen

Roskildavägen

TRANGELN

Kapellgatan

Köpenhamnsvägen

Pildammsvägen

Carl

RÅDMANS

Korsörvägen

Mariedalsvägen

Kronborgsvägen

Margaretavägen

PILDAMMSPARKEN

Pildammsvägen

VÄNGEN

Gust

Ängdalavägen

Pilakersg

DAMMFRI

Ribevägen

Roskildavägen

Batttista

PILDAMMARNA

UNIVERSITETSSJUKI MAS

John

Ericssons

KRONOBORG

väg

Bloom in the Park ●

MARGARETA PAVILJONGEN

▲ Hotel

● Restaurant

A

B

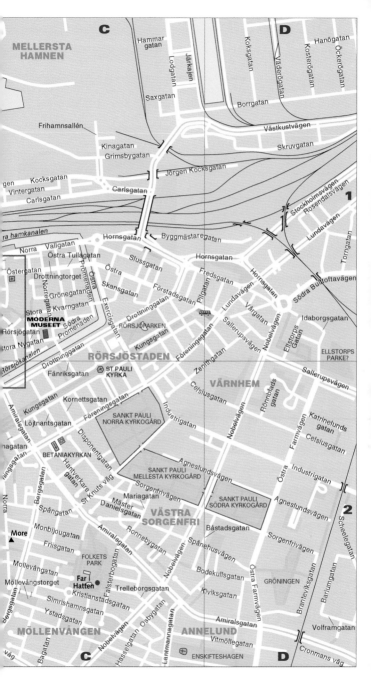

VOLLMERS ✿✿

CENTRE

CREATIVE • ELEGANT • INTIMATE

XX A/C ⇲

Tegelgårdsgatan 5 ✉ 211 33 – PLAN: E2
TEL. 040-57 97 50 – www.vollmers.nu
Closed 3 weeks January and Sunday

Menu 950/1350 SEK (dinner only) (tasting menu only) (booking essential)

Chef:
Mats Vollmer

Specialities:
Nettle soup with lumpfish roe and green tomatoes. Lamb with spring onions and potato. Strawberry, violet and cream.

An intimate restaurant with charming, professional service, set in a pretty 19C townhouse. The talented Mats Vollmer showcases some of the area's finest seasonal ingredients in set 4, 6 or 8 course menus of intricate and elaborate modern dishes, which are innovative, perfectly balanced and full of flavour.

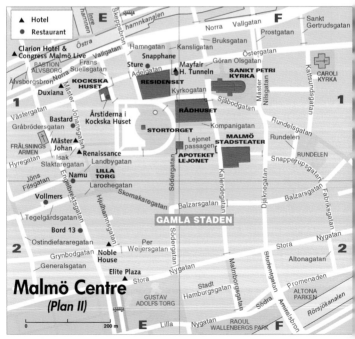

BLOOM IN THE PARK ✿

CREATIVE • DESIGN • CHIC

XX 🚫 🛜 A/C

Pildammsvägen 17 ✉ 214 66 – PLAN: B2
TEL. 040-793 63 – **www**.bloominthepark.se
Closed 24 December, Easter, Sunday and bank holidays

Menu 695 SEK (dinner only) (surprise menu only) (booking advisable)

Specialities:
Cod, wasabi, peas and grapefruit.
Variations of lamb with cabbage,
truffle and walnuts. Chocolate,
Sichuan pepper, passion fruit and
white chocolate.

A delightful lakeside lodge with a waterside terrace for drinks, run by an ebullient owner. There is no written menu or wine list; instead, the kitchen prepares a balanced set meal of modern dishes with international influences, which are accompanied by thoughtfully paired wines.

SAV ✿

CREATIVE • COSY • RUSTIC

XX 🍷 🚃 P

Vindåkravägen 3, Tygelsjö (South: 10.5 km by Trelleborgsvägen E22/E6) ✉ 21875
TEL. 072-022 85 20 – **www**.savrestaurang.nu
Closed 23 December-9 January, 21-24 February, 28-31 March, 22 June-31 July and Sunday-Tuesday

Menu 565/795 SEK (dinner only) (surprise menu only) (booking essential)

Chef:
Sven Jensen and Alexander Fohlin

Specialities:
Sugar beet, goat's cheese and
truffle. Pork with glazed parsley
root and gooseberry. Fermented
apple, pine syrup and apple sorbet.

Flickering candles and crackling fires provide a warm welcome at this charming 19C farmhouse. The two young chefs pick many of the ingredients and explain their surprise menu personally. Dishes belie their apparent simplicity – inspired combinations of tastes, textures and temperatures all play their part.

STURE

FRENCH • FRIENDLY • NEIGHBOURHOOD   XX

Adelgatan 13 ✉ 21122 – PLAN: E1
TEL. 040-12 12 53 – **www**.restaurantsture.com
Closed July, 21-31 December and Sunday

Menu 950/1195 SEK (dinner only) (tasting menu only)

Chef:
Karim Khouani
Specialities:
Foie gras with passion fruit and
nuts. Turbot with lettuce and
chicken stock. Apricot soufflé with
vanilla.

In 2016, accomplished chef Karim Khouani brought his exciting blend
of French and Scandic cooking from the country into the centre of the
city, reinvigorating this culinary institution. Top quality ingredients
are used to create inventive, well-balanced and sublimely flavoured
dishes.

BASTARD 😀

MODERN CUISINE • SIMPLE • TRENDY   ✗ 🛖 🄰🄲

Mäster Johansgatan 11 ✉ 211 21 – PLAN: E1
TEL. 040-12 13 18 – **www**.bastardrestaurant.se
Closed Christmas, New Year, Easter, midsummer, Sunday and
Monday

Carte 285/365 SEK (dinner only) (booking advisable)

Popular with the locals, this is a bustling venue with an edgy, urban
vibe. Style-wise, schoolroom meets old-fashioned butcher's, with
vintage wood furniture, tiled walls, moody lighting and an open
kitchen. Small plates offer nose-to-tail eating with bold, earthy
flavours; start with a 'Bastard Plank' to share.

NAMU

KOREAN • FRIENDLY • SIMPLE   X ⌂ AC

Landbygatan 5 ✉ 21134 – **PLAN: E1/2**
TEL. 040-12 14 90 – **www**.namu.nu
Closed Christmas, 31 December-1 January, Sunday and Monday

Menu 395/595 SEK (dinner) – Carte 355/550 SEK

Colourful, zingy food from a past Swedish MasterChef winner blends authentic Korean flavours with a modern Scandinavian touch. Dishes are satisfying – particularly the fortifying ramen – and desserts are more than an afterthought. Cookbooks line the shelves and friendly service adds to the lively atmosphere.

ÅRSTIDERNA I KOCKSKA HUSET ⑩

TRADITIONAL CUISINE • ELEGANT • HISTORIC   XxX ⌂ ⟡

Frans Suellsgatan 3 ✉ 211 22 – **PLAN: E1**
TEL. 040-23 09 10 – **www**.arstiderna.se
Closed July, Easter, 24-26 December, Saturday lunch, Sunday and bank holidays

Menu 525 SEK (dinner) – Carte 485/905 SEK

Set in softly lit, vaulted cellars, this elegant, formal restaurant is a city institution. Classic cooking proves a match for its surroundings, with local, seasonal ingredients proudly used to create traditional Swedish dishes.

ATMOSFÄR ⅈⓄ

SWEDISH • NEIGHBOURHOOD   ✗✗ ♿ 🏠 AK ⟷

Fersens väg 4 ✉ 211 42 – **PLAN: B2**
TEL. 040-12 50 77 – **www**.atmosfar.com
Closed Christmas, midsummer, Saturday lunch and Sunday
Menu 125/330 SEK – Carte 335/490 SEK

A formal yet relaxed eatery on the main road; dine at the bar, in the restaurant or on the pavement terrace. The menu consists of small plates, of which three or four should suffice. Fresh Skåne cooking is delivered with a light touch.

B.A.R. ⅈⓄ

MODERN CUISINE • WINE BAR •
NEIGHBOURHOOD   ✗ 🏠 ⟷

Erik Dahlbersgatan 3 ✉ 211 48 – **PLAN: B2**
TEL. 040-17 01 75 – **www**.barmalmo.se
Closed Easter, Christmas, Sunday and Monday
Menu 400 SEK – Carte 335/445 SEK (dinner only) (booking advisable)

This lively wine-bar-cum-restaurant in trendy Davidshall is named after its owners, Besnick And Robert. The interesting menu tends towards the experimental; expect dishes like Jerusalem artichoke ice cream with hazelnut mayo.

BISTRO STELLA 🍴

MODERN CUISINE • NEIGHBOURHOOD • PUB

Linnégatan 25, Limhamn (Southwest: 7 km by Limhamnsvägen: bus 4 from Central station) ✉ 216 12
TEL. 040-15 60 40 – **www**.bistrostella.se
Closed Christmas, midsummer, Sunday and Monday

Menu 395 SEK – Carte 240/635 SEK (dinner only)

A lively gastropub in a residential area not far from the Øresund Bridge. Its bright, cosy bar sits between two dining rooms and its menu features pub dishes like burgers, fish and chips and charcuterie platters. Cooking is rustic and tasty.

BORD 13 🍴

CREATIVE • WINE BAR • FRIENDLY

Engelbrektsg 13 ✉ 211 33 – **PLAN: E2**
TEL. 042-587 88 – **www**.bord13.se
Closed Christmas, Easter, midsummer, Sunday and Monday

Menu 375/675 SEK (dinner only) (tasting menu only)

Sister to B.A.R. restaurant, is the bright, spacious and stylish 'Table 13', which offers a set 3 or 6 course menu and a diverse selection of biodynamic wines. Original Nordic cooking has some interesting texture and flavour combinations.

FAR I HATTEN ⊪◯

SWEDISH · RUSTIC · FRIENDLY

Folkets Park ✉ 21437 – **PLAN: C2**
TEL. 040-615 36 51 – **www**.farihatten.se
Closed Christmas, New Year and midsummer

Menu 350 SEK – Carte 235/375 SEK (dinner only and lunch June-August)

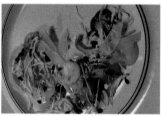

This unique restaurant is set in a wooden chalet in the lovely Folkets Park and has a cosy, informal feel, and colourful lights and regular live music in the summer. 4 or 6 course menus list well-presented classics with a creative edge.

MRS BROWN ⊪◯

TRADITIONAL CUISINE · WINE BAR · TRENDY

Storgatan 26 ✉ 211 42 – **PLAN: B2**
TEL. 040-97 22 50 – **www**.mrsbrown.se
Closed Easter, 24 December and Sunday

Carte 250/400 SEK (dinner only and Saturday lunch)

This retro brasserie's bar opens at 3pm for drinks and nibbles, while the kitchen opens at 6pm. Make sure you try one of the cocktails. Well-presented unfussy cooking has a modern edge and showcases the region's ingredients.

SNAPPHANE ⫴○

MODERN CUISINE • TRENDY • INTIMATE

Mayfair Hotel Tunneln • Adelgatan 4 ⊠ 211 22 – **PLAN: E1**
TEL. 040-15 01 00 – **www**.snapphane.nu
Closed 22-26 December, 1 January, Easter and Sunday
Menu 225/495 SEK (dinner only) (booking essential)

An elegant, intimate bistro with an open-plan kitchen at its centre. Innovative modern cooking uses top quality ingredients and dishes are well-presented, well-balanced and full of flavour. Service is friendly and professional.

CLARION H. AND CONGRESS MALMÖ LIVE

BUSINESS • MODERN • FUNCTIONAL

Dag Hammarskjölds Torg 2 ⊠ 211 18 – **PLAN: E1**
TEL. 040-20 75 00 – wwww.clarionlive.se
444 rm ⌑ – ♦ 980/2580 SEK ♦♦ 980/2580 SEK – 2 suites

The city's second tallest building affords a superb 360° view of the city; choose a bedroom on an upper floor for a view of the Øresund Bridge and Denmark. Kitchen & Table's eclectic menu combines American classics and international influences and you can enjoy a cocktail in the adjoining Skybar. The Ground floor houses an informal Mexican-themed restaurant and bar.

ELITE PLAZA

BUSINESS • CHAIN • MODERN

Gustav Adolfs torg 49 ✉ 211 39 – PLAN: E2
TEL. 040-664 48 71 – **www**.elite.se
116 rm ☕ – 🛏 977/2372 SEK 🛏🛏 1100/2712 SEK – 1 suite

Behind the wonderful period façade is a smart, up-to-date corporate hotel. Modern bedrooms are a good size: the best look onto a pretty square; the quietest overlook the inner courtyard. The British-themed bar has a pleasant pavement terrace.

MÄSTER JOHAN

BUSINESS • MODERN • PERSONALISED

Mäster Johangatan 13 ✉ 211 21 – PLAN: E1
TEL. 040-664 64 00 – **www**.masterjohan.se
Closed Christmas
68 rm ☕ – 🛏 900/2000 SEK 🛏🛏 1400/2500 SEK – 10 suites

A centrally located hotel, just off the main square, with a relaxed and peaceful air. Stylish, well-proportioned bedrooms have luxurious touches. Enjoy a locally sourced organic breakfast under the atrium's glass roof.

RENAISSANCE

BUSINESS • CHAIN • MODERN

Mäster Johansgatan 15 ✉ 211 21 – PLAN: E1
TEL. 040-24 85 00 – **www**.renaissancemalmo.se
128 rm ☕ – 🛉 995/2195 SEK 🛉🛉 1046/2345 SEK – 1 suite

A smart hotel on the site of the city's original food market: beamed ceilings and iron columns bring character to the modern interior. Bright, well-equipped bedrooms are quiet considering the hotel's location. There's a colourful bar and a simply furnished restaurant; modern dishes are created using local produce.

STORY STUDIO MALMO

CHAIN • BUSINESS • PERSONALISED

Tyfongatan 1 ✉ 211 19 – PLAN: B1
TEL. 040-616 52 00 – **www**.storyhotels.com
Closed 23-25 December
95 rm ☕ – 🛉 790/2190 SEK 🛉🛉 790/2190 SEK

The modern, well-equipped bedrooms of this hotel are situated on the top 5 floors of a 14 storey building next to the old port, and feature floor to ceiling windows. The ground floor eatery offers French cuisine, while the rooftop restaurant serves Asian dishes accompanied by beautiful city and harbour views.

DUXIANA

TOWNHOUSE • DESIGN • CONTEMPORARY

ΑΞ 송 ᕟ [A/C]

Mäster Johansgatan 1 ⊠ 211 21 – **PLAN: E1**
TEL. 040-607 70 00 – **www**.malmo.hotelduxiana.com
22 rm - 🛉 900/2315 SEK 🛉🛉 1130/2315 SEK, ☕ 70 SEK

A well-located boutique hotel; owned by the Dux bed company, who unusually use part of the lobby to showcase their products! Chic, contemporary bedrooms range from compact singles to elegant junior suites with a bath in the room. Staff are friendly and professional. Modern Swedish dishes are served at lunch.

MAYFAIR H. TUNNELN

TOWNHOUSE • HISTORIC • PERSONALISED

송 🕯

Adelgatan 4 ⊠ 211 22 – **PLAN: E1**
TEL. 040-10 16 20 – **www**.mayfairhotel.se
81 rm ☕ - 🛉 800/1900 SEK 🛉🛉 900/2200 SEK
SNAPPHANE – See restaurant listing

An imposing early 17C property steeped in history. Some of the homely, spotlessly kept bedrooms have spa baths. Breakfast is served in the impressive vaulted cellars dating back to 1307 and you can enjoy a complimentary coffee in the classical lounge. Snapphane showcases the latest local, organic ingredients.

MORE

TOWNHOUSE • BUSINESS • MODERN

Norra Skolgatan 24 ✉ 214 22 – **PLAN: C2**
TEL. 040-655 10 00 – **www**.themorehotel.com
68 rm ☐ – ♦ 895/1695 SEK ♦♦ 1095/2695 SEK

A striking aparthotel converted from a late 19C chocolate factory. The studios are modern and extremely spacious, with kitchenettes, sofa beds and light loft-style living areas. They are let on a nightly basis but are ideal for longer stays.

PARK INN BY RADISSON MALMÖ

CHAIN • FUNCTIONAL • MODERN

Sjömansgatan 2 ✉ 211 19 – **PLAN: A1**
TEL. 040-628 60 00 – **www**.parkinn.com/hotel-malmo
231 rm ☐ – ♦ 795/1395 SEK ♦♦ 795/1395 SEK

A good value hotel, well-situated on the Western Harbour beside the World Trade Centre and the Västra Hamnen waterfront. Bedrooms are spacious and well-equipped; the business rooms on the higher floors come with robes and have better views. The Bar & Grill offers easy dining.

NOBLE HOUSE

BUSINESS • FAMILY • FUNCTIONAL

🎿 ♿ 🛁 🏊 🚗

Per Weijersgatan 6 ⊠ 21134 – PLAN: E2
TEL. 040-664 30 00 – **www**.hotelnoblehouse.se
137 rm ☐ – 🛉 795/1550 SEK 🛉🛉 895/1750 SEK – 2 suites

A centrally located hotel, close to the bus station. Classically furnished, well-equipped bedrooms offer good value for money; ask for a room on one of the upper floors. There's a cosy lounge and a modern restaurant which serves traditional Swedish dishes.

KRAKAS KROG 🍴

CREATIVE • RUSTIC • COSY   ✗ 🍸 🍺 🏠 **P**

Kräklings 223, Katthammarsvik (Southeast: 39 km by 143 on 146) ⊠ 623 70
TEL. 0498-530 62 – **www**.krakas.se
Closed 1 October-15 June and Monday-Wednesday

Menu 475/1000 SEK (dinner only and lunch Saturday-Sunday) (booking essential)

An appealing countryside restaurant with a veranda overlooking the garden and a relaxed, homely ambience; its charming owner boasts an impressive knowledge of wine. Creative cooking utilises the best of Gotland's seasonal ingredients; flavours are intense and combinations stimulating and well-judged. Simple, stylish bedrooms complete the picture.

FÄVIKEN MAGASINET ✿✿

CREATIVE • INTIMATE • RUSTIC

XxX 🍴 🏠 P

Fäviken 216 ✉ 830 05
TEL. 0647-40177 – **www**.favikenmagasinet.se
Closed 2 weeks Christmas-New Year

Menu 3000 SEK (dinner only) (surprise menu only) (booking essential)

Chef:
Magnus Nilsson

Specialities:
Steamed mackerel, wild leaves and flowers. Roast mutton with ground dandelion root. Strawberries baked in pearl sugar with cottage cheese.

This remote yet idyllically set hunting estate offers a truly unique experience. The team hunts, forages, grows and preserves – and this bounty is put to stunning use in the multicourse dinner, using techniques rooted in Scandic traditions. All guests are served at the same time, by the chefs themselves. Bedrooms offer simple, rustic comforts.

HOTELL BORGHOLM ✿

MODERN CUISINE • CLASSIC DÉCOR • FRIENDLY

XX 🦪 ♿ AC

Trädgårdsgatan 15-17, Borgholm (North: 34 km by 136) ✉ 387 31
TEL. 0485-770 60 – **www**.hotellborgholm.com
Closed 1 January-10 March, Monday except June-August and Sunday

Menu 695/1295 SEK (dinner only and lunch Wednesday-Friday in winter) (tasting menu only) (booking essential)

Chef:
Karin Fransson

Specialities:
Perch with beans, tomato and garlic. Pigeon, celeriac, duck liver and lovage. Strawberries, warm elderberry and grapefruit mint.

A bright, spacious hotel restaurant hung with vibrant art. The self-taught chef offers a set 7 course menu based around superlative island ingredients. Classically based cooking is technically accomplished, artistically presented and demonstrates a mature understanding of balance and flavour.

HOTELL BORGHOLM

BUSINESS • FAMILY • CONTEMPORARY

Trädgårdsgatan 15-17, Borgholm (North: 34 km by 136) ✉ 387 31
TEL. 0485-770 60 – **www**.hotellborgholm.com
Closed 1 January-10 March

41 rm 🛏 – 🛉 1395 SEK 🛉🛉 1770/2090 SEK

HOTELL BORGHOLM ✿ – See restaurant listing

A long-standing, personally run and busy hotel in a pretty town; it's light and bright, with modern art on the walls. Compact, up-to-date bedrooms have wooden floors and modern furniture. The buffet breakfasts are comprehensive.

DANIEL BERLIN ✿✿

CREATIVE • FRIENDLY • INTIMATE

Diligensvägen 21 ✉ 273 92
TEL. 0417-203 00 – **www**.danielberlin.se
Closed 15 December-1 February, 18-30 June, Sunday-Tuesday and lunch Wednesday-Thursday

Menu 950/1850 SEK (surprise menu only) (booking essential)

Chef:
Daniel Berlin

Specialities:
Quail egg, pork and cumin. Turbot, bone marrow and beach plants. Honey frozen with sour milk, lemon verbena and colostrum.

A delightful 150 year old house in a quiet hamlet houses this charmingly run little restaurant. The highly skilled kitchen mixes New Nordic elements with a classic base to make the most of truly luxurious ingredients. There's a purity and subtlety to the 20+ dishes and the contrast in textures is memorable.

PM & VÄNNER ❀

CREATIVE • ELEGANT • INTIMATE XxX 🐝 ♿ AC 🍽

PM & Vänner Hotel • Storgatan 22 ✉ 352 31
TEL. 0470-75 97 10 – **www**.pmhotel.se
Closed July, Christmas, New Year and Sunday-Tuesday

Menu 795/1295 SEK (dinner only) (tasting menu only) (booking essential)

Specialities:
Langoustine with carrot, elder and langoustine emulsion. Lamb with onion and green asparagus. Rhubarb with meringue, lemon.

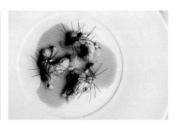

A formal hotel restaurant serving a 5 or 10 course set menu of sophisticated, original modern Nordic dishes. Their philosophy is based on 'forest, lake and meadow', and most of the ingredients come from surrounding Småland. An extraordinary wine list offers a huge array of vintages from top producers.

PM & VÄNNER

🏘

BUSINESS • LUXURY • DESIGN

🍳 ♿ 🆂🅿🅰 🛀 AC 🧗 🚗

Västergaten 10 ✉ 352 31
TEL. 0470-75 97 00 – **www**.pmhotel.se
74 rm ☕ – 👤 1490/1990 SEK 👥 1790/2190 SEK – 1 suite
PM & VÄNNER ❀ – See restaurant listing

A well-run, very stylish hotel with great facilities, including a bakery, a florist and a spa, as well as an appealing roof terrace complete with a bar, lounge, hot tub and plunge pool. Spacious, stark white bedrooms come with ultra-comfy beds and bespoke toiletries. The buzzy Bistro has a large terrace.

MICHELIN IS CONTINUALLY INNOVATING FOR SAFER, CLEANER, MORE ECONOMICAL, BETTER CONNECTED... ALL-ROUND MOBILITY.

Tyres wear more quickly on short urban journeys. **?**

TRUE!

You tend to accelerate and brake more often when driving around town so your tyres work harder!
If you are stuck in traffic, keep calm and drive slowly.

Tyre pressure only affects your car's safety. **?**

FALSE!

Driving with underinflated tyres (0.5 bar below recommended pressure) doesn't just impact handling and fuel consumption, it will shave 8,000 km off tyre lifespan.
Make sure you check tyre pressure about once a month and before you go on holiday or a long journey.

If you only encounter **winter weather from time to time** - sudden showers, snowfall or black ice - **one type of tyre** will do the job.

?

TRUE!

The revolutionary **MICHELIN CrossClimate** - the very first summer tyre with winter certification - is a practical solution to keep you on the road whatever the weather.

Fitting *2 winter tyres* on my car guarantees maximum safety.

FALSE!

In the winter, especially when temperatures drop below 7°C, to ensure better road holding, all four tyres should be identical and fitted at the same time.

2 WINTER TYRES ONLY =
risk of compromised road holding.

4 WINTER TYRES =
safer handling when cornering, driving downhill and braking.

If you regularly encounter rain, snow or black ice, choose a **MICHELIN Alpin tyre**. This range offers you sharp handling plus a comfortable ride to safely face the challenge of winter driving.

MICHELIN

MICHELIN
IS COMMITTED

▶ MICHELIN IS **GLOBAL LEADER IN FUEL-EFFICIENT TYRES** FOR LIGHT VEHICLES.

▶ **TO EDUCATE YOUNGSTERS IN ROAD SAFETY,** INCLUDING CYCLING, MICHELIN ROAD SAFETY CAMPAIGNS WERE RUN IN **16 COUNTRIES** IN 2015.

QUIZ

1 **TYRES ARE BLACK SO WHY IS THE MICHELIN MAN WHITE?**

Back in 1898 when the Michelin Man was first created from a stack of tyres, they were made of natural rubber, cotton and sulphur and were therefore light-coloured. The composition of tyres did not change until after the First World War when carbon black was introduced. But the Michelin Man kept his colour!

2 **HOW LONG HAS MICHELIN BEEN GUIDING TRAVELLERS?**

Since 1900. When the MICHELIN guide was first published at the turn of the century, it was claimed that it would last for a hundred years. It's still around today, with new editions published every year, along with online restaurant listings.

3 **WHEN WAS THE "BIB GOURMAND" INTRODUCED IN THE MICHELIN GUIDE?**

The symbol was created in 1997 but as early as 1954 the MICHELIN guide was recommending "good food at moderate prices". Today, it also features on the ViaMichelin website and on the Michelin Restaurants app.

If you want to enjoy a fun day out and find out more about Michelin, why not visit the l'Aventure Michelin museum and shop in Clermont-Ferrand, France:

www.laventuremichelin.com

INDEX OF...
RESTAURANTS 🍴

INDEX OF...
HOTELS

Tell us what you think about our products.

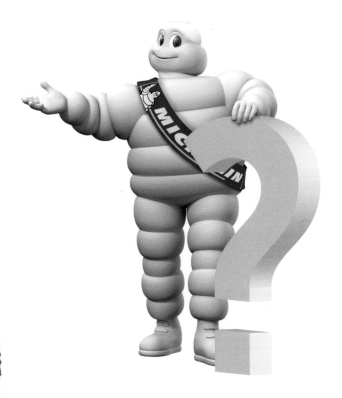

Give us your opinion

satisfaction.michelin.com

Michelin Travel Partner
Société par actions simplifiées au capital de 11 288 880 EUR
27 Cours de l'Île Seguin - 92100 Boulogne-Billancourt (France)
R.C.S. Nanterre 433 677 721
© 2017 Michelin Travel Partner - Tous droits réservés
Dépôt légal : février 2018
No part of this publication may be reproduced in any form without the prior
permission of the publisher.
Printed in Belgium
Typesetting: Nord Compo
Printing-binding: Geers Offset (Gent)